A PRACTICAL GUIDE FOR

HORSE OWNERS

Also by Jack Widmer

PRACTICAL ANIMAL HUSBANDRY
PRACTICAL BEEF PRODUCTION
PRACTICAL HORSE BREEDING AND TRAINING

A PRACTICAL GUIDE

for

Horse Owners

BY JACK WIDMER

CHARLES SCRIBNER'S SONS

NEW YORK

PRINTED IN THE UNITED STATES OF AMERICA
LIBRARY OF CONGRESS CATALOG CARD NUMBER 57-6072

The following sources supplied photographs:

F. J. Gosner, Los Angeles, page 18
Juanita Wilson, Asheville, N.C., 24
Times-Herald, 27
Carleton W. Patriquin, Boston, 31
Les Nelson, Wartrace, Tenn., 46, 48, 50-51, 52
Bernstein Studio, Hollister, Cal., 78

FOREWORD

Books, it would seem, are as unpredictable as horses. Horsemen agree that this earth offers few sights as wondrous as a foal romping with his dam during his first weeks of life. They are also quick to agree that there is nothing quite as foolish or frustrating as to attempt to prophesy the eventual mature horse that will develop from this appealing foal. The same seems true of books, especially books concerning the horse.

"Horsemen can't or won't read," was a favorite theme of the late Colonel Henry Leonard, one of our truly great horse show judges. "Other than for decorative purposes, the publishing of horse books is a waste of time, money, and effort." In the show ring we would never be so presumptuous as to differ with the good Colonel's judgment. In the matter of books, we must.

Practical Horse Breeding and Training, our first entry into the somewhat crowded, and at times very fast field of equine manuals (term of pregnancy 1939-41; foaled 1942) wobbled through its yearling and two-year-old years without enough promise to interest the Agua Caliente winter book. Then, as a three-year-old it began to find its stride and now, going to the post for its thirteenth season, it is still a reliable, if not spectacular performer. Although its sales have produced little more than a passing interest from the Collector of Internal Revenue, it is most gratifying to realize that it has run a good race and has become a minor standard among sporting books. It has been soul satisfying to see well thumbed copies in the offices of some of our better-known Kentucky studs, and even more pleasing to find it in the tack rooms of one or two horse stables, often the reverential dwelling of a "first" horse—a shaggy fellow, the loving property of a horseman of the future.

The book was written on our Horseshoe Ranch in Colorado, the home of some 30 Thorobred* brood mares together with the stallion *Pillory,* winner of the Belmont and the Preakness, where we were primarily concerned with the production and training of hunters, jumpers and polo ponies. The book was almost evenly divided into two major sections, breeding and training, and although the breeding information was applicable to all manner of horse, from the Welsh Pony to the Clydesdale, the training chapters were of little interest to horsemen other than those zealots of the polo or hunting field. Now, thirteen years since first publication, we find that the entire horse picture throughout the United States, and many other sections of the world, has undergone a considerable change. The thrill of hunting to hounds is still popular, but many a hunt has found it difficult to cope with the ever-increasing encroachments of the suburban problem. At this writing there are less than 3,000 riding to hounds, and those that are hunting are doing so less often. Polo has also suffered. There are less than half as many teams taking the field as there were a decade or so ago, due perhaps to rising costs and our present tax structure which make the maintenance of a first-rate polo string a most difficult thing indeed.

Despite all this, the use of pleasure horses has increased by leaps and bounds until today literally tens of thousands are in service. Interest in trail horses is tremendous, horse shows are booming, and riding clubs, sheriff posses, drill teams and common hacking have vastly increased the overall demand for light horses. As in many other sports, the reduction of the average work week, coupled with the increase in

---

* This spelling is used to differentiate between the proper name for the breed and the frequent misuse of the word such as its mistaken application to any purebred animal.

take-home pay has permitted many to devote time and money to the establishment of small stables and to ride the trails and halls throughout the country. Right or wrong, good or bad, emphasis on horses has shifted from the palatial estates of our fathers to the suburban dweller. The enjoyment of riding horses has gradually transferred from the few to the many. All this has made sections of *Practical Horse Breeding and Training* as obsolete as the brewery horse. Chapters on cost of horses and of their maintenance were written when the dollar was worth one hundred cents and are now ridiculous in their entirety.

Then too, our own interests have undergone something of a change. Living as we now do in San Benito County, the leading beef-producing area of California, we have become enthralled with working stock horses, roping ponies, parade and Quarter horses. Although our interest continues with Thorobreds (for this is an incurable disease), we find ourselves spending more and more time with horses other than hunters and polo ponies.

In addition, living within driving distance of most of California's top-flight horse show centers we have become increasingly interested in the American Saddle Horse, the light harness classes and the many Arabians that one finds so popular in the western states.

Advances in horse care from a veterinarian's point of view also dates *Practical Horse Breeding and Training*, and agricultural research in the scientific feeding of animals has made vast strides in the past 15 years. And so we have taken a new approach to an equine manual. We have attempted to broaden this work to reach the "new" horseman, as well as the "old" and to include information that we hope will be of interest to a larger group of readers. The chapters on breeding have been completely revised and brought up to date, while the balance of the book is entirely new.

So we give you *A Practical Guide for Horse Owners*, our 1956 entry, and hope that it will, even in a small way, answer a few of the multitude of questions that confront the horse fancier, and perhaps it will give added pleasure to that zealot of zealots, the equestrian.

JACK WIDMER.

Lime Kiln Farm
Hollister, Calif.
1956

TABLE OF CONTENTS

LIST OF ILLUSTRATIONS

A PRACTICAL GUIDE FOR

HORSE OWNERS

CHAPTER I

THE HORSE FOR YOU

It MATTERS little if you breed, raise and train your own horses, buy them on the open market or come by them through inheritance or through the "generosity" of a "friend"; the aim must always be the same—*the right horse for you.* The wrong horse has forced many a beginner (and a number of experienced horsemen for that matter) to lose interest because here the twain must, and often does not, meet. Even the most casual observer of the show ring, the hunting field, or the bridle path is quick to select those riders who are suitably mounted and are experiencing the only reason for being there—enjoyment. One does not have to be an intellectual giant to reason that any given horse may be an ideal mount for one individual and a living horror for another, for here what may be sauce for the goose is often poison for the gander. Yet, as discouraging as this may sound on first reading, "your" horse does exist, and by expending a bit of energy, a little common sense, coupled with a shot of luck, you are sure to find him and the search will prove very well worth while indeed.

As with anything else, there is one prerequisite to the search—you must know for what you are searching, and once knowing, you must be able to recognize the treasure at the search's end. At this point, perhaps, a series of questions that we have put to many a prospective horse owner will simplify matters.

1

What do you want a horse for in the first place? Is he to do a job of work—to gather cattle, to ride to hounds, to pull the sulky? Is he to be ridden by more than one member of the family and if so by whom besides yourself? Is he to be asked to enter the show ring (thereby making conformation important), or is he to be used as a park hack where an extra inch in back-length will make little difference? What sort of terrain is he to be asked to cover and at what speed? Is he to be sent fifteen miles per day, day after day, in lengthy trail rides over mountainous country where endurance and a sure foot are of primary importance, or will he be used on bridle paths in crowded cities where a knowledge of traffic is imperative?

To digress a bit, let us speak of experience, temperament and conformation—not of the horse, but of yourself. What sort of a rider are you; just how much horse are you capable of handling? With horses we may take the old adage quite literally—for often pride *is* followed by the fall; the fall by long and most unpleasant periods of hospitalization. Self-analysis is not simple. Judging one's own ability in any field is difficult, yet it can and must be done if one is to be a successful horseman.

Do you feel confident on a prospective mount, or do you feel, perhaps, that you are up on a bit too much horsepower? Beware of "overmounting" yourself. Ride a little less horse than you feel capable of handling at the moment and gradually increase your horsepower until you have reached the maximum of your ability.

Speaking of conformation, are you sound enough to handle the horse of your choice, and is your conformation compatible with his? What is so strange as to watch a 200-pound man riding a 14.2-hand Arabian, only because our gentleman was enthralled by Carl Raswan's delightful book, *Drinkers of the Wind,* and is in love with this particular little mare that groans under his middle-aged poundage. Or worse yet, glance for a moment at our little lady of 90 pounds who doesn't begin to have strength of arm to handle the cold-jawed 17-hand hunter that is exactly the proper color to accentuate her flowing and hennaed locks. Of course, these are extreme examples, yet sad to say, they are more common than exceptional.

Are you temperamentally equipped to handle a young animal; to school him, to cope with the dozens of misfortunes that go into the training of a youngster? Or are you short of temper and should therefore be satisfied with a "made" horse, the result of proper training by someone of more even disposition, time and experience? When you ride, are you interested in "riding" every minute, or do you lean to the more social type who prefers to chat with your companions and therefore require a horse capable and willing to do much of the thinking for the pair of you?

Naturally, funds available will have much to do with the horse of your choice—one can spend from $25 to $25,000—yet the old adage, "It's not the original cost, it's the upkeep," is even more true of the horse than of the wife. A poor horse eats fully as much as a good one—often more—for nervous, high-strung horses are unsatisfactory keepers, while placid, well-adjusted animals will keep fat and sassy on a tennis court. So an additional few dollars will be well spent in the original purchase. It is also elementary to point out that board bills running upwards from $50 per month are common, and that the horse fancier may just as well be feeding an animal that returns enjoyment rather than a beast that gives little but trouble, a rough ride and a sour disposition in return for oats, hay and bedding.

Love, the poet would have us believe, is the acme of human emotion. Be this as it may we must concede that love of human for human might very well be a "thing of beauty." We may even go so far as to concede that love of horse for horse might be highly desirable. But that's as far as we go. We know that love of human for horse is a most dangerous pastime and often leads to the prison of no escape. Affection we find is a far different word, and affection for one's horse is not only desirable, but often, in the case of the young animal, a prerequisite. Yet to fall hopelessly in love with one's horse—never! One sees too many misfit horses housed and fed in luxuriant quarters (due to the mistaken love of an owner which oddly enough is more often than not strictly a one-sided affair) who should have long ago been sent to the hounds. It is most difficult to dispose of an object of love, even when unrequited; yet if the horseman is to be successful, horses, as all livestock, must be culled when they no longer can perform their functions adequately, or must be sold when the owner discovers that he has made a mistake in selection. As to the broken-down, worn-out animal, how much better to put him down at once; how much more humane to send him to the green pastures rather than permit him to waste away despite comfortable surroundings.

Assuming that we have a general knowledge of what sort of horse we want, or better yet, realizing that the horse that we now have is not "our" horse, we are ready to undertake the search. First off, let us not be afraid to scream for help. Strange indeed is the fact that even though the average horseman is willing to admit ignorance in other matters, he is a horseman first, and beyond question an excellent judge of horse flesh—in short, an authority.

We have had many a chuckle recalling Carroll Howell, Professor of Animal Husbandry at the College of Agriculture of the University of California (and in our opinion *the* authority on animal nutrition) when, opening a course on the feeding of the horse, he asked those students who had had a horse for more than 30 days and less than six months to raise their hands. Hands shot up all about the lecture hall, for his students were of the "short course" variety and all passionately interested in horses.

"You," smiled the good professor, "are excused. At this stage of the game there is little that I or anyone else can teach you about horses."

Regardless of breed desired (we shall discuss them in detail in the following chapters) soundness of the animal in question is the paramount issue. If the horse is not sound of wind and limb, how can we expect him to perform his duty adequately? Here, a consultation with a competent veterinarian may be highly desirable, yet the reader is warned that beyond being able to pronounce a horse sound, many veterinarians leave something to be desired as judges of horses. It would be equally as foolish to assume that all veterinarians are good judges of horse flesh as it would to assume that all orthopedic surgeons are shrewd judges of the human race. Yet we must know that the horse is sound; that he stands squarely on four good feet; that he is free from ring-bone, bog-spavin, and the countless other deformities to which the horse is subject. It would not be amiss to remember the advice of the Bedouin Chieftain who, when undertaking the teaching of his son to judge horses, began his instruction with the horse placed behind a tent flap with only the feet and fetlocks being exposed.

"If you cannot pass perfect judgment on the four feet, go no further," was his advice, "for it matters little how perfect the rest of the animal might be. Without feet you have no horse and *your* feet will be blistered by the scorching sands."

Perhaps the most satisfactory starting point in the search for the right horse is the farm that breeds, trains, and sells finished horses. On such an establishment the buyer has an excellent opportunity to observe what is going on. Usually the prospect's dam and sire are in residence, the training techniques of the farm may be studied, and the general care and handling of the horses observed. True, these farms are not found in large numbers, for many breeding establishments train few horses, preferring to sell them as youngsters to those who specialize in this art. Yet they can be found. A post card to any of the horse clubs and associations will produce a full list of their members, while many of these clubs maintain up-to-date listings of horses offered for sale which they will be happy to supply the interested buyer.

Operators of such stud farms fully realize that their continued success depends largely on the satisfied customer and thus are less likely to misrepresent the horse or to attempt to palm off a highly undesirable animal on the uninitiated. Many such establishments are pleased to send photographs and descriptions (thus often saving the buyer long abortive trips), and most of them will be frank enough to inform the prospective purchaser when they do not have the type, age or sex desired.

Contrary to general belief (and this is a carry-over from the days of the migrant trader) the average established horse dealer is an honest man. He fully realizes that "return business" plus word-of-mouth advertising is his stock in trade, that a dissatisfied client screams much louder than a satisfied one; and so he can usually be depended upon for an honest appraisal of a horse in question. He is to be found in most any horse country and often frequents horse fairs and shows, riding halls and training establishments. If he does not have "your" horse, he will know where it can be obtained and a small commission is often money well spent. Having been a dealer for many years, he knows all the tricks of the trade (they are legion), and many a wise buyer has thrown himself upon the mercy of a reputable dealer and lived to be most thankful.

Horse trainers are also a good starting point. Every horse center, and certainly every area where horses are raised or used in any number, can offer at least one professional trainer who, besides the string of horses that he is custom schooling, usually has a horse or two about the place that he is offering for sale. In addition he probably knows every horse within a hundred-mile radius and is often an excellent source of information. A local horseshoer also has firsthand knowledge of his working area and is often a worth-while contact.

Public auctions are usually not a very satisfactory source of supply for the "made" horse. If one is interested in the purchase of untrained young horses or is looking for breeding stock (together with a veterinarian's certificate), the auction is the ideal market place; but to those about to purchase a "working" horse, one that will be the "right" horse, the public auction is a risky business. Seldom are horses sold here other than "as is" or at the end of the halter shank, and the purchaser has little if any redress. Here one should remember *caveat emptor*. The Roman was no fool.

The practice of a trial period in the sale of horses is rapidly growing in popularity. Any reasonable breeder, dealer, or trainer, who professes to have the buyer's interest at heart (together with his own pocketbook) and having nothing to hide, welcomes a 30-day trial as quickly as he would permit a veterinarian's examination. From the buyer's standpoint this is an ideal arrangement. He is usually permitted to remove the horse to his own establishment (sometimes a deposit is indicated, insuring the return of the horse in the same general condition) to try him on the home grounds and for the purpose that he is intended. Should the animal prove undesirable in any way he is returned and little damage is done on either side. How much better than a hasty trial and inspection, a rapid purchase and a lengthy disappointment.

As in anything else, the horseman often receives exactly what he pays for. There is no set market for horses as we find in cattle, sheep or other classes of livestock. A horse is worth exactly what the buyer is willing to pay and is worth that figure only during the instant of sale. Bargains in horses are of course not entirely unknown, but they are rare indeed and a "cheap" horse often proves extremely expensive.

A first-rate mechanic may purchase a very used automobile and make a profitable investment. His knowledge of motors and things mechanical, coupled with his experience of knowing where to look for defects, will permit him to make an intelligent selection and should trouble develop, he is in a position to make the necessary repairs with minor expense. The same is true of the qualified and experienced horse trainer. He, too, knows what to look for at the time of purchase, and his experience will permit him to make corrections in faulty training habits. Here again we must ask the same old question: How much do you know about horses? Can you prove it?

Beware of the oft repeated assurance of the seller when he pats you on the shoulder and says, "All this animal needs is a lot of hard riding and you're just the horseman for the job. Surely you'll be able to iron out the wrinkles."

Make sure that you are that horseman, for even though the purchase price may be low (and the horse is the proper color), he may turn out to be the most expensive purchase since the Hope diamond as well as being a highly dangerous brute to have around the place. Many a horse trainer keeps his establishment solvent, and his children in college, by retraining "bargain" horses that have proven too much horse for "just the right horseman." It is elementary to say that retraining fees added to the original "bargain" quickly mount to a total that would have purchased the "right" horse at the very beginning.

If you do not qualify as a professional trainer beware also of the spoiled horse; that animal that has been improperly started; the big Thorobred who is a bit too slow for the track; or the hunter that has become unmanageable in the field. Any competent and honest trainer will be glad to tell you that he would much rather start with a colt that has never seen a man rather than to correct bad habits of long standing. As for the ex-race horse, beware again. He has been taught little but to fly out of a starting gate, to run at full tilt, sometimes in a straight line. It is true that top trainers have developed some excellent hunters and open jumpers from rejected race horses, but their lifetime batting average is more like ours than Joe Dimaggio's.

Above all beware of the "friend" who wants to present you with a horse. "Never look a gift horse in the mouth." . . . Tommyrot. Look and then look again. We remember the wise old Kentuckian who startled a large and impressive dinner party with the cry:

"Good Lord. I forgot to lock my stables. I must be excused."

"Stables? Locked?" his hostess repeated. "Are you afraid of horse thieves here in Kentucky?"

"Goodness no, madam. I'm merely afraid that some of my neighbors, taking advantage of my absence, will leave me a horse or two to feed. Hay is expensive, I'm nearly to the bottom of the oat bin and I've enough worthless horses of my own to feed without taking on anymore old crocks."

Above all, despite all the help that you will receive, you must be the final judge in horse selection. Remember well the old story of the fetching evening gown: how appealing it was when properly filled by the startlingly proportioned manikin, and how ridiculous it looked on Aunt Matilda. Remember well that even though the professional rider makes it all look so simple when he demonstrates the horse and takes him over four-foot jumps, that you are buying the horse, that you will be doing the riding—not he.

Remember well that riding is the professional's business, that he sat his first horse at three, that perhaps he would look just a bit ridiculous were he to get out of his own backyard and attempt to remove an appendix, to build a bridge, or preach a sermon. No, there is nothing for it but to get up on the horse yourself. After all is said and done, this is a horse for *you*. Get the proper one for your own individuality.

CHAPTER II

BREEDS AND TYPES

CHOICE of breed is almost as important as type within any given breed. Obviously, individual breeds have been developed to perform definite jobs of work, and the purpose to which we are to commit our horse will have much to do with breed selection. Many fantastic claims are made by certain breed associations and clubs. However, we will attempt to point out the obvious advantages of the various important breeds, together with what we feel might be their shortcomings. Here we are very apt to make few friends and perhaps influence fewer people, yet it is high time that someone takes an unbiased appraisal of certain of the breeds and types.

Some Thorobred enthusiasts will insist that the Thorobred can do anything that any breed of horse can do from running a mile to plowing a furrow and do it better—wrong. The Quarter horse fancier will explain that the Quarter horse is the only breed suitable for working cattle—wrong again. The Arabian breeder will explain that all Arabians have unbelievable stamina and are the only breed fit for endurance trials and long trail rides—doubly wrong. Morgan people insist that the

New England horse is suitable and unbeatable for any purpose from racing to the sulky to heavyweight hunting, and they too have been known to go completely overboard in their claims.

Perhaps this understandable enthusiasm is a healthy thing; perhaps the never-yielding enthusiasm of proponents of every breed is a governing factor in the improvement of such breeds and is therefore not only excusable but desirable. However, the inexperienced horseman in his search for the right horse within the right breed will be somewhat confused after he has listened to a number of enthusiasts all touting their own particular breed of horse.

No breed, regardless of how long it has been established, has been 100 per cent standardized as to type regardless of conflicting claims to the contrary. Not even the proponent of the Thorobred (a noun indicating a particular breed, not an adjective indicating pure-bred), despite its 260-year-old registry, can claim that all Thorobreds conform to a definite type. There are Thorobreds, and there are Thorobreds. Some are of the racy elongated type, others short-coupled and deep-muscled, making excellent polo ponies and often first-rate cow ponies. And so if 260 years cannot produce a "true type," what chance has one of the younger breeds to do so in a matter of 20 years, as is often the claim.

In choice of breed, the horseman will find himself in much the same quandary as did the five-year-old boy at the candy counter with his proverbial nickel, for propagandists for various breeds have become so proficient as to make the late Herr Goebbels seem a rank amateur by comparison. We feel that the type within the breed is by far the most important point to consider, and of course the individual within the type is the ultimate ingredient that will spell success or failure.

A word about registration papers. Just how important are they, and how much additional actual cash should be paid for the registered over the unregistered animal? We feel it was put rather neatly by a gentleman of our acquaintance when he said: "Registration papers never harmed a good horse and never helped a poor one."

If we are going racing we are by necessity restricted to the registered Thorobred, for not only is he supreme in this field, but all horses entered on our recognized tracks must be registered with the Jockey Club. If we are going into breeding (regardless of breed) registration papers are of high value. If, on the other hand, we are primarily interested in a park hack, a parade horse, a hunter, polo pony or a western horse, then registration papers may be of dubious value. Sex, too, may be a determining factor in this regard. If we purchase a gelding as a pleasure horse and are not particularly interested in the show ring (some classes are restricted to registered animals), we would place little emphasis on a scrap of paper. If, however, we purchase a filly, papers may develop into a sales point when we are through with the animal as a riding companion and wish to sell her as a brood-mare prospect.

When we are confronted with the sales talk: "But this horse is registered," we might well ask: "Registered where—in what stud book?" The past three decades have produced more horse registration associations than have the past three centuries. We have associations that will register for type regardless of color; we have associations that will register for color regardless of type; and we seem to have some stud books that issue registration papers presumably for the registration fee.

The Palomino is a classic example in the "how confusing can you get" department. Mrs. Doreen Norton in her most attractive volume, *The Palomino Horse*, lists six separate and distinct Palomino registration associations in the United States alone, with several others in foreign countries. A qualified Palomino may conceivably be registered in any or all of these six domestic associations. In addition, if the animal in question is of the type desired, he may be registered by the American Quarter Horse Association (there were two registrations for Quarter horses up until not too long ago); while if the other half of his blood can be traced to the Thorobred he may also be registered in the Half-Breed book, which calls for the registration of all animals of ½ or more Thorobred blood. We now have a rather large fistfull of papers.

All this leads to considerable confusion, and has done much to minimize the intricate value of horse registration. And so, where is the horse registered and how many dollars is this actually worth to the purchaser? Is he registered in some national "book" where purity of the breed is of primary consideration, or is he registered in one of dubious value where the actual registration fees are the primary reason for the existence of the association? It has now reached the ridiculous point where we see advertisements in horse magazines advertising horses for sale that are "guaranteed triple registration," and we wonder if we are being offered a horse or are we off on a paper chase. True, many of the new "books" that are working diligently on a "new" breed may eventually develop a true strain, yet this dream is, in some instances, at least, a century away. As one friend of ours put it, "Why can't we start a registry for bay horses, especially with black points? There ought to be a book!"

There are literally hundreds of manuals devoted to the individual breeds that are readily available to those wishing to pursue the matter in detail, and we see little point in rehashing material that long ago was overcooked. Instead, we prefer to devote our allotted space to what one may reasonably expect from the individual breeds: what to look for; what to guard against; obvious strengths, weaknesses and past performance. In many instances we will agree with the claims of individuals and associations; in others our experience may force us to disagree. We will attempt to shy away from the classic mistake made by many writers when they erroneously believe that the most satisfactory manner in which to build up "their" breed is by running down all others. It has always amused us to realize that so many propagandists insist on going so far in their claims as to appear ridiculous, whereas the enumeration of the true strengths of any given breed would have been ample to have presented a very strong case for the breed in question.

Being in somewhat of a quandary as to the order in which the breeds would be best presented, we cast about for suggestions. Should age of breed be a factor, should we risk listing them by popularity, or should our personal likes and dislikes influence the order of battle? Finally, the logical, alphabetical order was suggested. We liked the idea, and certainly we could not be accused of favoritism here. Now, it has just occurred to us that the little lady who offered the helpful suggestion is a breeder and strong advocate of, all things, THE AMERICAN SADDLE HORSE.

THE AMERICAN

SADDLE HORSE

The American Saddle Horse is exactly that. He was developed in Tennessee, Kentucky and Missouri and when properly trained, he is as good a ride as anyone could expect under certain conditions. We are more than pleased to agree that he has no peer as either a three- or five-gaited saddler and we are willing to overlook some claims of the *aficionado* as to his ability as an exceptional hunter, topflight polo pony and cow horse, despite the occasional individual that is the exception that sometimes proves the rule. Having practically every known breed of light horse somewhere in his background, he is the classic example of selective breeding, inbreeding, and ruthless elimination of those individuals that did not meet the type until today he has been developed into a breed that has surprising uniformity in conformation and way of going.

On tanbark, he puts on an unbeatable show when it comes to flashiness and there are few thrills in the equine world to compare with watching the $10,000 Stake at the Kentucky State Fair. Having been developed for ease of going—he was developed as a plantation horse for the landed gentry and their overseers—he is a most comfortable ride (outside the show ring) and is rightfully becoming more and more popular for the pleasure-seeking equestrian. He can be developed into an excellent driving animal (to light harness), and he is without equal as a combination horse—to ride and drive.

15

The champion light harness horse of many shows is *Blacazhell* judged by many as being one of the best light harness horses ever to step on tanbark. He is an American Saddle Horse of *Denmark* breeding and is shown after winning the $1000 Stake at the Santa Barbara Horse Show. Miss Jody Haden, daughter of owner Bill Haden, is in the buggy.

Linden Pride by *And-Then-Some,* a classic example of the five-gaited American Saddle Horse in action. *Linden Pride* has won in all major show rings and is considered an outstanding example of the breed.

The Saddler, as he is sometimes called, may be divided into two general classifications—show horses and working horses—and although the two look much alike, here all resemblance ends. The show animal is strictly a performer, almost from the moment of foaling. He is taught animation (often with the whip) from the time he is weaned, and he is schooled in a much different manner than is the animal destined to become a pleasure horse. The show animal is seldom ridden in the company of other horses, he is diligently schooled in his gates in private, and his feet are permitted to grow so long (for increased height of action) as to make him a dangerous ride for the average horseman on anything short of tanbark. He spends practically his entire performing lifetime in a box stall wearing his tail set, and he requires more time and effort to keep him in show condition than any animal known to man with the possible exception of the World's Ten Best Dressed Women.

All this artificiality has been most misleading to those whose knowledge of the American Saddle Horse is limited to observing those pampered pets of the tanbark as they give their spectacular performance in the ring. All this has caused the Saddler to be misjudged. For every top show performer there are literally hundreds of American Saddle Horses who are making a first-class living on the bridle paths of the nation. It would seem comparable to a man from Mars, having wandered into the Copacabana, concluding that all the world's womanhood is faithfully represented by the damsels of that famous chorus.

The working Saddler (and this does not imply that the show animal does not work—how he works!) with his feet sensibly trimmed, and often with natural rather than nicked tail which requires the wearing of the uncomfortable tail set, makes an ideal hack; is not difficult to train; and gives his owner a comfortable ride. It is true that some animals, started as show prospects and having been found wanting, have found their way into the working class, but the beginner must be warned that this is a transition best accomplished by a trainer of considerable experience. Conversely, some working Saddlers have been developed to the point where they have done very well in smaller shows, but this, too, is the exception, for the big time is really THE BIG TIME and the competition so tremendous as to make it impossible for only the best of professionals to give a creditable performance on a horse that has never been asked to do anything but perform a well-rehearsed act.

As everyone knows, the American Saddle Horse is further classified into five- and three-gaited specialists. With the walk, trot and canter being the natural gaits of all horses, these three gaits are those shown by the "three gait." The addition of the slow gait and rack, both man made, are the result of much schooling and give the "five gait" his name. As for the light harness horse, many three and five gaited horses have been developed into excellent competitors.

The American Saddle Horse has been developed to the point where they usually stand from 15 to 16.2 hands in height and vary in weight from 900 to 1200 pounds depending on condition and development. They are found in many colors (there is even an American Golden Saddle Horse Association, which translated, means a Palomino colored horse of American Saddle Horse breeding and performance), but they are predominantly bay, black, brown and chestnut with the flashy chestnut being the most fashionable. They are short of back, and their feet, in comparison with other breeds, have been developed to enable them to tolerate the long toe and to carry the weighted quarter boots that are used to increase the height of action of the five-gaited specialists. They are flat and strong of bone which keeps them from going sour too quickly when asked to rack for long periods of time, a gait most comfortable for the rider and certainly most uncomfortable and damaging for the horse; and their manes and tails have been developed into the flowing elegance that makes them the peacocks of the horse world.

There has been much controversy regarding the practice of nicking the tail and subjecting the animal to months in the tail set. Humane societies have, for years, fought this practice, some states going to the extreme of legally banning it, although with little evident enforcement, and the practice has been a bone of contention with horsemen the world over. Many also feel that the practice of inserting a piece of well-chewed ginger into the animal's anus is also a bit on the gamey side—spectacular tail carriage or not. There can be little question that the tail set practice is anything but comfortable for the animal; however, as long as it is necessary if one is to show in the ring, the operation of nicking should be performed by a most experienced veterinarian and the tail set adjusted by someone of great experience. Here is no place for the uninitiated, for not only may the tail be damaged for life, but the added discomfort to the horse is often over-emphasized by the "do it yourself" amateur.

From a disposition point-of-view the Saddler is almost without a peer in the equine world. If handled considerately while a foal, then as a yearling and a two-year-old he is not difficult to train (training will be taken up in detail in later sections), and the Saddler may be made into a very usable horse by the amateur trainer. He has enough generations of breeding behind him (and ease of training has always been a predominant factor with the exception of those destined for the highly competitive show ring) to guarantee an even disposition. If properly trained in the first place with minimum use of the whip, he is usually very trustworthy, and he has been developed into excellent children's mounts and is found in numbers in the more select riding academies.

THE ARABIAN

The Arabian has done more for the race of horses than any other breed. Directly or indirectly his blood is found in every breed of light horse from the Thorobred to the Quarter horse, for he was the basis of both the Thorobred and the Spanish horse, the first horse brought to the North American Continent by the *Conquistadores*. The Arabian is the result of most careful breeding through several centuries, this development being conducted by the Bedouin Tribes that drifted into Arabia, rather than by the original Arabian Tribes with whom they intermarried. These nomadic, undersized Bedouins did not invent the horse as is sometimes thought; however, the influence of Bedouin horsemanship is felt today throughout the horse world. He kept few records of the genealogy of his own family (for this was a minor matter), and yet he could and would recite the pedigree of his war mare, through the only important line to him—the female, from the days of Mohammed or before. He held the stallion in small regard, except as a mate for his mare, and he would rather walk than ride a male. He mistakenly believed that a mare once bred to an inferior stallion was contaminated for life, and thus many excellent mares were retired from the stud and never permitted to produce. He would never strike a horse and would never sell a mare, the result being that for many centuries only stallions were exported from Arabia, and we therefore trace our Arabian crosses to the male line.

Among other sterling characteristics, the disposition of the Arabian horse is directly traceable to having been made an intricate part of the Bedouin family. The Bedouin was and is fanatically fond of horses and the war mare was held in high regard. The Arabian therefore makes a wonderful pet and why shouldn't he? He's been a pet for centuries and rivals the dog as man's companion. Having been raised in his master's tent, and having from one to six camels as his wet nurses, he has been developed to such a point of intelligence as to have few rivals in the equine world. Their characteristics have been handed down to the other breeds until today most students of the horse are quick to credit the intelligence of any of the breeds to the horse of the desert.

Having been produced on difficult terrain and having been forced to survive on grazing lands that are anything but lush, the Arabian has not attained the size that is desirable for many jobs of work. He seldom stands much over 15.1 hands at the withers, and he is more often found in the 14.1- to 15-hand category. He sometimes weighs less than 900 pounds and rarely does he exceed 1000. Yet despite his lack of size, he's a rugged little fellow and has been bred true to type for so many centuries that he has acquired an extraordinarily unique appearance. Once the amateur is able to recognize the Arabian he will always recognize him, and even the presence of Arabian blood in other breeds. His true colors are grey, bay, chestnut and brown, and now and then he is found in those rare and valuable colors—pure black or white. He is never found as a spotted horse, contrary to circus posters who proclaim their trick horses as being "Arabian" and, of course, imported directly from Sheik so-and-so's desert tribe.

With good reason Arab fanciers insist he is the most beautiful of horses, for he possesses a great deal of style and quality. His head is in the classic tradition, being short from poll to the softest of muzzles, very broad between the eyes, and the face definitely dished. His eyes are large, set low in the head and kindly, and his ears are short and extremely refined. His neck is slim and arched and runs well back into the withers. Having one less lumbar vertebra than other breeds, he has a strong well-knit back which assists him in carrying extreme weight for his size. He is well sprung of rib, carries his tail high and, having less hoof and leg trouble than most of the breeds, is perhaps the soundest of horses. Respiratory diseases are practically unknown in the

Arabian, and he has the ability to travel long distances and to make very quick recovery from exertion. He has been used very successfully to cross with lesser breeds, and more often than not his get are larger than himself.

Thanks to the Kellog Arabian Stud Farm of California and other breeders, the Arabian has been imported to the United States in considerable numbers during the past 25 years, and the issuance of several stallions by the late United States Army Remount Service has done much to spread Arabian blood throughout the Western states.

Since the days of Christ, the Arabian has been known for his endurance; yet in all fairness, it must be pointed out that many horses of other breeds have defeated the Arabian in endurance contests. The Arabian breeder will quickly point out that these other breeds have traced their endurance qualities to their Arabian blood, and therefore prove rather than disprove the point.

Lack of size has somewhat handicapped the Arabian in the hunting field and for other equine tasks wherein height and weight are required. He is anything but a first-class jumper and does not do too well in performance classes in the show ring when shown against other breeds. Yet he is a "big little horse" and is ideal as a pleasure horse, sometimes develops into a good polo pony, and has often been made into a top-flight rodeo and roping horse. He is extensively used as a parade horse (often with rider in Arabian costume and appointments) and is found being ridden in drill teams, sheriff's posses and is without equal as a child's or lady's mount. He is not difficult to train, and as has already

The outstanding Arabian mare *Roda*, bred by Prince Mohamed Ali of Cairo, Egypt, and owned by Margaret Shuey of Asheville, North Carolina. The remarkable fact about *Roda* is that this photograph was taken when she was 18 years of age and as sound as the day she was foaled.

The Arabian stallion *Rifage*, owned by the Van Vleet Arabian Stud of Colorado, is here shown working cattle in a cattle drive that started at 5300 feet and went to timberline at 13,000 feet. High-altitude Arabians indeed.

Arraff, with Harold Brite in the saddle. Cutting cattle without bridle is ample proof of the versatility and intelligence of the Arabian. In the background we see Senator George W. Malone of Nevada hazing on *Al-Marah Wabre*.

been pointed out, is one of the world's finest pets. He loves to play, yet is kindly under saddle, and if properly schooled is most obedient. He possesses an excellent flat-footed walk, and although he is sometimes criticized for a short "choppy" trot, he has a most comfortable canter and hand gallop. He's a great little horse and has been the most significant single factor in the improvement of all manner of light horse breeds.

THE MORGAN HORSE

The Morgan Horse, the oldest of the important American breeds, is a creature of circumstance. There would never have been a Morgan breed had not Justin Morgan, a Vermont farmer-school teacher, become sufficiently angered to make the long trek into Massachusetts to collect a debt of long standing. Had he been successful in his aim—the collection of the hard money of the realm—the Morgan horse might never have been developed—certainly never under that name. But instead of cash, Justin Morgan returned to the rugged hills of Vermont with a three-year-old gelding and a two-year-old colt. The three-year-old has long since passed into obscurity, but the two-year-old was to make the name Justin Morgan immortal in the horse world. It was this two-year-old, who somehow had been overlooked when the other colts on the Massachusetts farm had been altered, that was to become the only male in history to propagate a breed of horses; it was this two-year-old colt bearing the name of his new owner that was to immortalize the name of Justin Morgan.

The abortive debt-collecting trip took place in the fall of 1795, a year to be well remembered in the equine history of the United States, for not only did *Justin Morgan,* the horse, sire all the foundation stock of the Morgan breed, but he was also instrumental in establishing the Standard Breed, the Tennessee Walking Horse and the American Saddle Horse, all three breeds depending to a greater or lesser extent upon Morgan blood.

There seems little doubt that *Justin Morgan,* the horse, carried considerable Thorobred blood, probably through a stallion called *True Britton,* but it is also apparent, from his shaggy fetlocks and muscular development, that he carried considerable cold blood, possibly from the Dutch horse that had been developed in New Amsterdam. There is also little question that *Justin Morgan* was one of the most remark-

29

able stallions that ever lived, regardless of breed, for he was so pre-potent that his get were unmistakably *his*, regardless of the quality or conformation of the mare to which he was mated. His get were all Morgans, and it is astonishing to realize that all the members of his family showed family likeness from birth, a uniformity of type so strik-ing as to make them immediately identifiable.

Countless romantic stories of both Justin Morgan, the man, and *Justin Morgan*, the horse, are found in horse literature—most of them unreliable, many of them conflicting in every degree. All kinds of theories concerning the foundation sire have been published, and there is very little likelihood that the true story will ever be disclosed. We do know that *Justin Morgan*, the horse, was dark bay in color with no white markings, and although we know little of Mr. Morgan's height, we know that the horse stood a mere 14 hands and weighed in the neighborhood of 900 pounds. He was used, and sometimes misused, for every common equine task on the farm, was driven to harness, put to the plow and was used as a saddler to carry his master to the local tavern when the day's work was done. That he was of great heart and spirit was unquestionable, for it is conceded that he could "outdraw, outwork, outtrot, and outrun every horse that was ever matched against him." That he changed hands repeatedly is a matter of record, and that many of his owners were far from kind to the grand little fellow has also been proved without question. It is equally certain that none of his owners realized the value of the horse for he was often sold for less than $200, and it is agreed that none of his owners had the slightest indica-tion of how important the little stallion was to become to the future of the American horse. Even though *Justin Morgan* was bred to literally hundreds of undesirable mares and was often forced to make his own living in the hilly regions of Vermont, he established a breed of horses that has left its mark on the Pampas of Argentina, the Bush of Australia, and, of course, throughout the entire North American continent.

Mrs. Rodger Ela of the Townsand Morgan Horse Farm in Vermont with her mare *Sadwin*. *Sadwin,* one of the best known of modern Morgans, has won countless classes both to the cart and under saddle.

A section of the 100-mile trail ride of the Green Mountain Horse Association of Vermont. Dr. Wilson Haubrich (right) winner of the Horsemanship Award rides together with his son and daughter in this delightful annual event.

In the beginning the Morgan was noted predominantly for his prowess as a trotting horse, establishing all trotting records of the day. The breed was then stockier than those of the present, for during the past 25 years the emphasis has been placed on saddle type—longer neck, more definite withers and considerably more refinement of the legs and head. This has been accomplished by selective breeding and the elimination of some individuals that were subject to coarseness.

In the early days of the settlement of the Western plains, a number of Morgan stallions made the long overland trek and this, coupled with the latter-day Remount Service, has left an influence of Morgan blood in most of our Western cow country. Being noted for their great endurance qualities, coupled with a strong degree of soundness (a direct transmission from the fiery little foundation sire), the Morgan was a great success in the wide-open-spaces and did much to breed up the quality of Western cow ponies. Many of these Morgan-native mare crosses (Morgan stallions on native mares of Spanish origin) found their way to polo fields and did very well in high-goal early-day competition.

As we know the Morgan breed today, they stand from 14.2 to 15.2 hands at the withers, a considerable improvement from *Justin Morgan* who stood a mere 14 hands, and they usually weigh from 1000 to 1200 pounds. They are closely coupled, short backed with considerable bottom, depth of body and staying power. They are broad of chest, deep muscled, and have a good way of going. They are predominantly brown and black, but are also found in chestnut. In contrast to other breeds, white markings are not a very predominant feature. However, when bred to Western Indian ponies, paints and pintos have often been the result.

To the many Morgan fanciers the breed is one of "beauty, spirit and docility." After over a hundred and fifty years of up-breeding, the

Morgan certainly has attained these ends, and as the Morgan Horse Club points out:

"In the Morgan, beauty, spirit and docility are unexcelled. And these attributes are almost all-inclusive. For beauty encompasses color, conformation (head, body, limb and foot), style and action. Spirit means fire, energy, life. And docility makes the beauty and spirit of the horse serviceable."

Be this as it may, the Morgan Horse certainly has his place in the horse world. Although never destined for the hunting field, some Morgans have been developed to a high degree for the pursuit of hounds, and many excellent children's hunters carry a predominance of Morgan blood. As for the polo field, once the aim of many Morgan breeders, the slower Morgan has given way to the Thorobred when more and more speed was required.

The Morgan has done very well under light harness and as combination horses for both driving and riding. The Morgan usually has an excellent disposition and is therefore not difficult for the amateur to train. They are easy of gait, and most of them have also become popular on dude ranches where a combination of style and safety are of predominant importance; for the same reason they are well liked as riding academy mounts.

In addition to their history of serviceability, the Morgan will be long remembered for what they have done for breeds that came later. The Standardbred can trace many of its qualities to the Morgan and it is not surprising to learn that *Greyhound*, 1:55¼, the world's champion trotter, has five crosses of Morgan blood; that the Tennessee Walking Horse owes much of his style and way of going to the Morgan and that the flashy American Saddle Horse might never have been developed were it not for that creature of circumstance—the Morgan Horse.

THE STANDARDBRED

The present-day Standardbred has no peer as a trotter or pacer. So completely has the breed absorbed all competing breeds that he stands alone. He is the world's fastest harness horse, and he has popularized harness racing—the poor man's sport of kings. Since the very beginning, many an owner of a trotting champion has been "of the people" from the original Astors of New York, "those prosperous German butchers" who migrated to the new world in the late 18th Century, to the average man of today who finds fine harness racing within the limits of a modest American income. Where a Thorobred enthusiast interested in establishing a flat racing stable of quality is confronted with an initial investment running into thousands if not hundreds of thousands of dollars, the trotting tyro can often pick up a likely youngster of good breeding for less than a thousand dollars, his sulky and tack for another five hundred, and he's in business. Nor does he have to contemplate high training, jockey and feed bills, for normally he will do his own training and driving, and his Standardbred will usually be a much easier and less expensive keeper than will the Thorobred counterpart.

The Standardbred is practically the only breed of horse wherein all emphasis has been placed on performance. Some critics of the Thorobred will be quick to argue that this is also true of the Thorobred. Not so, for every Thorobred racing today, there are dozens who are used for other purposes—hunting, jumping, polo, hacking, etc., where many other requirements are of far more importance than mere speed. The Standardbred is asked only to trot or pace at maximum speed and therefore conformation becomes a secondary consideration.

The Standardbred is the result of more than a hundred and fifty years of utility breeding. Produced originally to trot and pace under

35

saddle, and later converted to roadsters and light harness, racing was at first a secondary consideration—speed was not. In the days before the automobile, great pride was taken in fast road horses that worked the lanes and byways of the nation and a "brush" (impromptu contest) was enjoyed by the butcher, the baker, and the farmer as well as the sportsmen who bred for speed only and preferred the racing strips and tracks.

As has been pointed out, the Morgan Horse had much to do with the development of the Standardbred, together with the Canadian Trotter, the Black Hawk, the Clays, the Narragansett Pacers and, of course, the Thorobred. It was the imported Thorobred stallion *Messenger* (whose direct lineage is traceable to the *Darley Arabian*) who became the foundation sire of all modern trotters and pacers. Yet all of the above breeds and families have been superseded by the get of one horse—*Rystellyk's Hambiltonian,* whose family today is the only one of real significance. So well known did *Hambiltonian* and his get become that the name *Hambiltonian* and Standardbred have become almost synonymous to the point where many people feel that they know what a *Hambiltonian* is, but would have difficulty defining Standardbred.

The Standardbred performs in two distinctive gaits, the trot and the pace. Seldom has any one horse become proficient in both and the usual custom is to train each animal to trot or pace when his "natural" gait becomes apparent, usually at two years of age. The pace is, of course, a two-beat gait wherein the lateral legs move together, while the trot is the lifting of one front foot and the opposite hind foot at the same time. In past years, the pacers were the faster of the two and held most of the records. Today, however, times for trotters and pacers are so close as to have removed most of the difference that twenty years ago was so apparent.

Mrs. Ruby Tucker with the champion pacer *Lulu Tod* ready for an early morning workout. *Lulu Tod* is owned by Harmon Snibley and has done well on the circuit.

The U-shaped training
barn so popular with
harness racing trainers.
The open court is excellent
for "cooling-out," while the
low overhanging roof in
front of the stalls offers
protection from the
elements.

Early morning at the Bay Meadows track where the youngsters are being schooled at the starting device.

Having been bred primarily for speed with little thought given to conformation or uniformity of type, the present-day Standardbred will vary from 14.3 to 16.2 hands and will weigh anywhere from a light 800 to a heavy 1250 pounds. The predominant color is bay, although they are found in greys, browns, and chestnuts. The racing custom of going three one-mile heats in a given afternoon has been a factor in the production of endurance and soundness is often coupled with the endurance quality. By necessity, they have been bred for excellent feet and legs, although many are criticized for cycle hocks (too much curve of the hock joint) and are often cow hocked (hocks pointed together). They are usually short of back in comparison with the Thorobred and are often steep of croop. They sometimes stand "over at the knees" but they are large of knee and hock joint and stay sound for years. *Greyhound,* perhaps the greatest of his breed and possessing more world's records than any horse of any breed that ever lived, retired in 1940 after seven years of hard campaigning and retired completely sound and still possessing all his speed. He was retired for the good of the game for there just wasn't any competition worthy of stepping onto the track in his presence. What Thorobred flat racer could boast such a record?

In the early days of the present century, many Standardbred stallions were shipped to the West to improve the Western harness horse, and many were bred to Western native mares to give more speed and size to Western saddle horses. In later years, countless numbers of these half Standardbred mares were mated with Thorobred stallions (usually U.S. Army remounts) and produced top-flight hunters, polo ponies and mounts suitable for army chargers. The Standardbred also contributed to the development of the American Saddle Horse who owes much of his height of action and facility in various gaits to the trotter.

The thrill of thrills, the finish of a close pacing mile.

Today, the Standardbred is produced primarily for light harness racing, a sport which is booming from coast to coast in the United States and gaining in popularity throughout the world. Many racing plants are operated exclusively for trotters and pacers, while several flat racing courses stage meetings for harness horses as well as for flat racing. County and State Fairs throughout the nation are partial to harness racing, and it would be difficult for the harness horse fancier to live anywhere in the United States that did not offer a source of competition within a reasonable distance.

Perhaps the greatest advantage of harness horses over those racing on the flat is the tremendous joy and sense of achievement that the amateur derives from the training, schooling and racing of his own stock. As has been pointed out, the amateur need not have a terrific Dun and Bradstreet rating to enjoy the sport, and there is no greater thrill in competitive horsemanship than to be in your own sulky, breezing along behind a horse of your own training.

We suppose it is natural that something of a feeling of animosity exists between Thorobred and Standardbred people. Both sides no doubt have their strong arguments, but we feel that the entire situation was summed up rather neatly, from a Standardbred point-of-view, at least, by one of our better known trotting trainer-drivers when he said:

"You Thorobred gents amaze me. You spend years of time, thousands of dollars, on a likely prospect. You school him at the starting gate, you teach him to run his heart out and then when he is ready for the question, you sit a hundred-pound midget up on his back, offer a few words of advice and go sit in the stands. Now you're hoping against hope that the midget doesn't have a brain to match his physique. From then on there's nothing you can do but pray and cuss.

"Now take the harness man. He too spends years of time, but hundreds instead of thousands of dollars on a prospect. He schools and trains the youngster himself and when it's time for the question, he puts on his silks, lights up a fresh cigar and crawls onto his sulky. He's got the horse under control all the time and he can change his race plan as the situation develops. He has that thrill of all thrills as he pounds around the track, his horse's tail brushing against his face. If he wins it's to his and his horse's credit. If he loses, he doesn't have to blame some lame-brain jock. What's more, a few additional years or a little increase of his waist line doesn't put him on the shelf. Goodness me, man, I'm pushing sixty-five and I expect to race another ten years. Yep, you Thorobred men really amaze me."

Only a few days old, and what a charmer. Straight of leg and a showman from birth. A fine example of the Tennessee Walking Horse as a youngster.

THE TENNESSEE WALKING HORSE

The Tennessee Walking Horse, also known as the Plantation Walking Horse was developed for the same reason as was the American Saddle Horse—comfort for the rider who must spend long hours in the saddle day after day and usually during the hot cultivating and harvesting months of the summer. As a Plantation Walker they were justifiably popular. Their running walk (up to nine miles per hour) permitted them to cover many miles daily, and their straight "rocking chair" canter was ideal for covering ground at a rapid rate and still staying between the crop rows. All this was done with considerable comfort for the rider and the Plantation Walker did much for the agricultural development of the South.

Although the Plantation Horse has been earning a good living for over a hundred years, it was not until 1935 that the Tennessee Walking Horse Association was formed and a stud book originated for the registration of those animals that qualified for the standards set up for the breed. Not long thereafter many of the larger horse shows presented classes for the Walker and they quickly became popular with contestants and audiences alike. It was then, in our humble opinion, that the trouble for the breed first became apparent.

As a Plantation Walker the horse was ridden with natural mane and tail, but soon after they became popular on the horse show circuit, set tails began to appear—a direct imitation of the American Saddle Horse. This was bad enough, but not the end of it, for soon some breeders, more interested in blue ribbons than in utility, began to breed for "refinement" with more and more emphasis placed on what they termed "quality" and less thought given to the only reason for having a Tennessee Walking Horse—the rare and valuable gait, the running walk.

47

This attractive weanling Walker is a fine example of his breed. He is of good bone, refined conformation and shows the calmness so predominant with the Walker.

It is a happy thought that not all breeders have gone completely over-board in this direction, that a great percentage of Walkers are still true to the old type and that the nicking and setting of tails has not become as universal a practice as it has with the American Saddle Horse.

"After all, why make imitation Saddlers out of our Plantation Horse?" one of our better known and more sensible Tennessee Walking breeders demanded. "If people want a horse with a set tail and a Saddle Horse conformation, why not breed Saddlers and be done with it?" Why not indeed.

The Tennessee Walking Horse (so named because his development took place in central Tennessee) is a cross of many breeds of light horses. Some trace their lineage to the Morgan, many to the Thorobred, and they are closely related to the Standardbred and the American Saddle Horse. The Narragansett and Canadian Pacers, no doubt, played an important role in their development and are responsible for the running walk gait that makes them a breed apart. This running walk is an inherited gait and cannot be taught; however, additional speed and form may be accomplished through diligent schooling.

The breed usually runs from 15 to 16 hands at the withers, and they normally weigh from 1000 to 1250 pounds. They are short backed, carry their heads low in comparison to the American Saddle Horse, and they are extremely strong of leg. Their knees and hocks are larger than those of other riding breeds, and they are sometimes criticized for being too sloping of the crop. They are long and sloping of shoulder, which adds to the comfort of the rider, and they have a head more on the order of the Standardbred than any other breed. They are excellent of disposition, are easily trained and are most popular with the amateur owner-trainer. Their running walk being a natural gait makes their schooling much less difficult than the Saddler who must be taught two of his five gaits, and therefore their schooling is not difficult for the tyro.

Tennessee Walking Horse
yearlings at Harlinsdale Farm,
Franklin, Tennessee.

The stallion *Happy Days K.*, property of Mr. and Mrs. Emmett Darby of Oklahoma City, with Vic Thompson up. He is an excellent example of the show-type Tennessee Walking Horse.

During the past fifteen years they have become increasingly popular on the Western range. No cowpuncher worth his salt will ever permit a horse to trot, a most uncomfortable gait for those who sit tight in the Western saddle. The horse of the West must either walk or canter, and the wise cow-poke never runs his horse on his way to or from a job of work. Realizing that he has many miles to travel and further realizing that when he gets to his destination he may need all the horse he can get to cut cattle, to run back fence crawlers, or to perform other everyday cow-country chores, he walks his horse to the job, uses him unmercifully when he has to, and then again walks him home. What better horse can he therefore have than the Walker who, with his comfortable ambling, running walk, can cover up to nine miles per hour and do it with little strain on himself or his rider. Even at the flat-footed walk the Tennessee Walker will cover a good five miles per hour, and he has thus become so popular with the Westerner that it is virtually impossible to find a good Walker on the sale lists.

He has also made his name as a parade horse, as a mount for members of sheriff's posses, and for usual pleasure horse work. He is easily broken to drive and he is in demand as a combination horse where he may be driven as well as ridden. He lives long—25 years is not exceptional—which seems proof enough of an even disposition and a quiet outlook on the world. Having considerable size, the Tennessee Walking Horse has become an all-purpose horse for the small farm. He makes an excellent light draft animal, doesn't object to raking up a bit of hay and is ideal for children both to ride and drive. Many Walking mares have produced outstanding saddle mules (when bred to a Jack) and these mules often inherit the running walk of their dams.

The Walker is never ridden to double bridle, instead, he is shown with single reins, and if properly trained, never requires a heavy hand. Extreme bitting is seldom necessary (we have seen several Walkers work well while wearing nothing more severe than a halter) and a soft leather curb strap is preferable to the chain. They are taught to neck-rein and are ideal as a trail horse.

They have been bred for flash in color running to chestnut, bay, black, grey, brown and roan, and several first-rate Palominos have been developed that carry a predominance of Tennessee Walking Horse blood. Several of these Palomino-colored Walkers have been produced in California and considerable effort is being expended to develop Walkers of Palomino color for use on Western trails and in Western parades.

As time goes on, as the maintenance of the new stud book develops enough generations for standardization, it is our thought that the Tennessee Walking Horse will vastly increase in popularity. They are a wonderful horse for their purpose and should go far on bridle paths and in the show rings of America. They are utility personified and give their owners much pleasure. True, they are unsuitable for the hunting field and too slow and ungainly for polo, but as a pleasure horse for general all-around riding, they certainly have their place in the horse world.

THE THOROBRED

To the casual week-end horseman the Thorobred horse means one thing—speed. As far as it goes, this is very true, for the Thorobred has so completely dominated both flat and hurdle racing as to have eliminated all serious competitive breeds over a century ago. Yet to the horseman who knows his horses, the Thorobred is much more than a mere speed demon. He is unbeatable as a hunter or jumper, no polo pony worthy of the name is less than ¾ Thorobred, and most top-flight rodeo arena horses, cutting horses, and top cow ponies carry a lot more Thorobred blood than most people realize. The Thorobred cannot be touched as an endurance horse; he is tops in dressage; and he is without rival in any equitation sport that calls for heart.

As has been pointed out in every one of dozens of books on the history of the Thorobred horse, the Thorobred traces his male line to the *Godolphin Arabian*, the *Darley Arabian*, and the *Byerly Turk*, all stemming from the Arabian of the Bedouin Tribes. It is fairly well established that these foundation sires were imported to the British Isles between 1690 and 1725 and were mated with the rugged little English native mares and that this cross worked so well that the resulting breed had more to do with the establishment of all light horse breeds than any other.

During the past 25 years it has, for some strange reason, become fashionable for advocates of various breeds to disclaim the active presence and strong influence of Thorobred blood in their particular breed. This is almost as foolish as it would be for Thorobred people to deny the presence of Arabian blood in the English horse. Some Quarter Horse people have gone so far as to advertise Quarter horses for sale "carrying less than 1/16 Thorobred blood." How they could possibly

Thorobred racing is big business indeed. Hollywood Park, Inglewood, California, is but one of many elaborate racing plants throughout the nation, a true criterion of the value of Thorobred racing in the sporting scene.

derive such a figure is most difficult to understand, for there are so many mares and stallions of unknown or unproved origin who have produced Quarter horses in the not too distant past and who very likely carried a great percentage of Thorobred blood. Where else would they have obtained their great speed (for a short distance), where else would they have found their intelligence, their heart and their quality? Nor is this denial of Thorobred blood limited to Quarter Horse people. Some writers on the American Saddle Horse have written reams to minimize the importance of the Thorobred in their particular breed, and the same is true of some of the advocates of lesser breeds.

A tabulation of *foundation sires* of various breeds, all *registered* Thorobred stallions, is of interest in illustrating the far reaching effect of Thorobred crosses:

Standardbred	*Messenger*
American Saddle Horse	*Denmark*
Quarter Horse	*Janus*
The Morgan Horse	*True Britton* (thought to be the sire of *Justin Morgan*)

In addition to the above *foundation sires,* Thorobred blood is most evident in the Tennessee Walking Horse, several of our Western types, and even the Welsh Pony who traces his ancestry to a small Thorobred stallion who was turned out with a group of pony mares. That the Thorobred gave style and refinement to most modern breeds is without question, and like it or not, most breeds today would be of little consequence without it.

The first Thorobred to be imported to the United States from England was the stallion *Bulle Rock* who made the hazardous journey in 1730, and there has been a continual importation of the best of English blood since that date. As has been shown, the influence of Thorobred blood in all breeds of American horses is considerable, and it was augmented by the United States Army Remount Service which was in operation between World War I and World War II. This service, knowing a good thing when they saw it and being interested in producing sound, top-quality horses to be used in a national emergency, placed Thorobred stallions of good type with agents throughout the country, infusing the best of Thorobred blood with the grab-bag of native mares from Maine to California and developing animals that will forever have an influence on the American horse.

The great turf champion *Swaps* chops two-fifths off his own world's record for the mile and a sixteenth. Time 1:39 flat with *Swaps* carrying 130 pounds. At the time of this photograph *Swaps* was the holder of five world's records and has proven himself the ultimate in Thorobreds—speed at a distance and the ability to carry weight.

The Remount, realizing that there are Thorobreds and there are Thorobreds, was careful to select stallions of the calmer if not the faster families. Long criticized as "hot bloods" the Thorobred has had to live down the erroneous impression that they were good for nothing but racing. The Remount did much to educate the average ranchman and farmer and to dispel this fallacy. It is true that certain highly inbred Thorobred families are a bit on the "hot" side, and yet other families are docile, train easily, and make excellent pleasure horses.

In conformation, the Thorobred varies greatly, but not as greatly as in the case of the Standardbred. They run all the way from the elongated, long-legged speedsters of the track to the compact short-backed, deep muscled type that have produced the best polo ponies ever to stand outdoors as well as stock horses without serious competition. Many Thorobreds of the latter type have been passed off as Quarter horses, and it has been amusing to many Thorobred people to have clean-bred Thorobreds referred to as perfect Quarter horse types.

The present-day Thorobred varies from 15 to 17 hands at the withers and from 900 to 1350 pounds in weight. They are usually chestnut, brown, black, bay or grey and some have roan hairs in their coats. They are thin skinned and carry considerable quality. The good ones are deep of chest and large of heart girth, have long slender necks and display much refinement of head. It goes without saying that some families bred for speed and speed only are far from this desired standard of conformation, and some are apt to be on the "weedy" side—long, lean and brittle.

The half Thorobred, together with the maintenance of the Half Breed Stud Book (for animals of 50 per cent or more, and less than 100 per cent Thorobred blood), has done much for the horse of America. The hunting field is primarily made up of "half breeds" ranging all the way to 31/32 pure-breed. They are the world's finest hunters, as the

The Thorobred is, of course, unsurpassed as a polo pony. Many cross-breeds have been tried, but in the final analysis the Thorobred dominates the polo field as he does the track.

Irish hunter has proved for generations, and they are without serious competition in the show ring as either hunters or open jumpers.

Many half-breeds have also been highly successful in stock horse classes and some of the nation's better Palominos carry upward to ⅞ Thorobred blood, usually the result of breeding a chestnut stallion to a Palomino colored mare. There is no reason why the reverse would not produce Palominos (the Palomino stallion to a chestnut Thorobred mare); however, most Thorobred mares are of too great a value to be bred to anything short of a Thorobred male.

In days gone by, the Thorobred produced the best cavalry horses, most of which were upwards of ½ Thorobred, and officers' chargers were either clean bred Thorobreds, or animals carrying a predominance of Thorobred blood. Many of our best Army pack horses were also part Thorobred, and some of our best Army pack and riding mules had considerable blood of the English horse tracing through their dams.

And so, despite statements to the contrary, the value of the Thorobred as an individual and as the foundation stock for most of our other breeds cannot be over-emphasized. As Mr. John T. Cain, III, general manager of the Denver National Western Stock Show, one of the leading stock horse centers of the world, puts it, "The only time that Thorobred blood hurts a horse is *when it ain't there!*" How true, brother, how true!

THE WESTERN HORSE

The Western horse has been in business on the North American Continent longer than any other type or breed. First used by the *Conquistadors* as cow ponies when they unloaded their original Spanish cattle in the New World, he has been doing business at the same old stand for the past four hundred years. Being of Spanish blood (with a strong Arabian and Barb background), he was the basis for the Indian pony who pursued the Pony Express rider who was also mounted on a Western type of Spanish origin. He was the mustang of the plains country, the tough little Cayuse of the original rodeo circuit, the foundation of the Army charger and the descendant of the Western horse now known as the parade horse, the cutting horse, the roping pony, and the Western trail horse.

Oddly enough, he is more popular today than ever before, for the past 25 years have seen a wild scramble towards riding clubs (in Western regalia), sheriff's posses, mammoth horse parades, mounted drill and square dance teams, and just plain hacks that are ridden under Western saddle not only in the Western states but in practically every state in the Union. Of course, the Western horse is still busy at his primary job—working cattle, but it is interesting to note that today there are far more Western horses than there are herds of cattle for them to work; that many a Western horse is asked to perform duties far distant from the running down of a calf or the cutting out of fat beef during the fall round-up.

Perhaps this was brought about by Hopalong Cassidy, the late Tom Mix, or the antics of Roy Rogers, or was it just that ever present desire for adventure in every man, for many a suburban dweller who has never been closer to a cow than 100 yards is the proud owner of a Western type horse and delights in the sheriff's outfit or the costume of the Spanish grandee whom he emulates in fiestas, parades or festivals. Some more experienced horsemen may smile a bit as they observe a $50 horse carrying a $5,000 saddle and a rider long on custom and short on horsemanship; yet this is the exception, for the Western horse is a working horse and performs his duties very well indeed. Roughly, they are classified into cow ponies, parade horses, and show horses, and they are made up of many breeds, types and colors that have become popular with the Western type rider.

THE QUARTER HORSE

The Quarter Horse has been developed into the best cow pony ever known to man. He is without serious competition as a rodeo performer, calf-roping horse, cutting horse, or race horse for distances of ¼ mile or less, from which, of course, he derives his name. He is honest, has plenty of "cow sense" and loves his work. To the connoisseur, there is no sight as heart warming as watching a first-rate cutting horse work cattle, and there are many Quarter Horse people who swear that a good cutting horse reads brands as well as his master. Be this as it may, we do know that cutting horses have been developed to a fine degree of expertness and once shown the cow to be brought out of the herd, will do so with little if any guidance from the rider.

The story goes that the Quarter Horse was first evolved as a sprinter in the early days of the American Colonies (perhaps as early as 1650) when the young "bloods" of the Eastern Seaboard used them in match races over quarter mile racing strips cut from the virgin forests. That these early Quarter Horses were mainly of Thorobred blood is without question, and the breed today owes its speed, durability and intelligence to the English horse.

"*Steeldust*," said to have been a Thorobred stallion, was brought into Texas, and as many refer to the Standardbred as a "Hambiltonian," many Quarter Horses were known (and still are) as "Steeldusts" in honor of this important sire. The same is true of the "Billy Horse" named after the stallion *Billy*, said to have been a descendant of *Steeldust*. Yet regardless of origin (and quarter horse enthusiasts argue on all sides of the question), it has been reasonably well established that the Quarter Horse of the East, bred to the native mares of the Southwest (usually of Spanish blood) has resulted in the present-day Quarter Horse, most popular in all manner of cow country.

65

David J. Findlay on his champion Quarter Horse *Jeffy*. *Jeffy* is a top roping performer, has the disposition of a puppy and is an important member of the Findlay family.

This excellent Quarter Horse, the property of Taylor Pillsbury, is a classic example of the short-coupled, deep-muscled Quarter Horse of the West.

The Quarter Horse breed can roughly be classified into three major categories. First, we have those developed strictly for racing—those speed merchants that have run the quarter mile in 21.2 seconds and are bred with little thought given to conformation, manners, or cow sense. They vary greatly in type (as do their Thorobred and Standardbred counterparts) but they can fly for a Quarter mile or less, and they are being raced more each year with many Thorobred race meetings devoting a considerable share of their purses to sprinters.

Quarter Horse racing is becoming more and more popular and the reason is this finish of a 400-yard race. The track customers get a tremendous run for their money, for all sprints offer close finishes, most of the "photo" variety.

The second type is the show animal, the contestant in the hundreds of Western type horse shows held throughout the land. Here conformation and performance are of equal importance. They are shown in countless fairs and horse shows, in roping classes, cutting contests, etc., not only throughout the West, but of more recent date in many Eastern communities that have brought the dude ranch to the Eastern seaboard.

The third category is the working Quarter Horse who makes his honest living on the ranches of the West and Southwest. Here he is without competition and many cattlemen would rather part with their right arm than their favorite cutting horse. Their quick start and stop and their ability to cover ground rapidly are essential for the cutting and turning of cattle, and the same burst of speed has made them invaluable for calf-ropers and steer-doggers where the split second start is often the difference between success and failure.

The Quarter Horse usually stands from 14.2 to 15.2 hands at the withers and weighs from 1000 to 1200 pounds. He is deep muscled, broad of chest, thick of neck (in comparison to some Thorobreds and most other breeds) and is sometimes criticized as being flat of wither and coarse of head. He is usually of good bone, has strong well-formed feet and carries much of his weight forward of the saddle. To the uninitiated he is often criticized as being "lumpy of muscle," but it is this heavy muscular development that gives him his terrific start and short burst of speed. He has, through necessity, learned to live off the land, is therefore an easy keeper and requires little pampering. He is not difficult to train, has an even disposition and makes a very acceptable pet. Many a ranch youngster has been taught to ride by some elderly Quarter Horse, for they often live to be 25 to 30 years of age and stay remarkably sound throughout a long and useful life. They are sure of foot, make excellent trail horses and have justly become popular in mountainous areas.

At this writing there is a disturbing movement afoot to restrict Quarter Horse registration to those horses of limited influence of Thorobred blood. This scheme is entirely impractical, for much Thorobred blood is carried by the better Quarter Horses. After all, if the Thorobred is removed, what is going to remain? We feel that the problem will take care of itself without legislation by the Quarter Horse Association, for without Thorobred blood the Quarter Horse will retain practically none of its speed, little of its intelligence and a small percentage of its heart. The best Quarter Horses are of definite Thorobred type (best from both a conformation and performance standpoints), and it is our thought that good Quarter Horses will always show their Thorobred ancestry if they are to remain a useful and important breed.

It is never too young to start with a Palomino. Here our two-year-old cowboy rides in his first Western Horse Show—Bolado Park, California.

THE PALOMINO

The Palomino is not a breed or a type—it is a color. The horse may be of Thorobred type, he may be a registered Tennessee Walking Horse, he may be predominantly Morgan, American Saddle Horse, or Quarter Horse, or a combination of these and other breeds. The Palomino (even those registered in one of the numerous "books") may be of almost any shape or size as long as he meets the color classifications set down by the terms of the various associations. Consequently we have all kinds of Palominos ranging from the very useful to about the poorest bits of horseflesh that ever stood outdoors.

This is in no way intended to infer that there is no such thing as a good Palomino—there are and there are many. One of the finest and most perfectly molded horses that we have ever seen happened to be a Palomino, but he would have been an outstanding individual and performer (to us, at least) had he been chestnut, bay, brown, black or grey. To us color does not make the horse. To the Palomino *aficionados*, it does.

As color is the most important characteristic of the Palomino it might not be amiss to quote the requirements for registration as put forth by the Palomino Horse Breeders of America:

"1. A good riding horse of any of the recognized breeds, exclusive of draft and Shetland types.

2. Dark eyes and black skin.

3. White, ivory, or silver mane and tail.

4. Body coat gold, the gold standard that of a newly-minted gold coin. Because of the variation in shade in different localities, acceptable horses may have body coloring either five shades lighter or darker than the gold standard."

73

It becomes immediately perceptible from the above that color is all that really matters. The term "good riding horse" may mean one thing to one person—something entirely different to another. Yet, a first-rate Palomino of the "proper" color is a beautiful thing to behold. They are extensively used in the Tournament of Roses Parade that precedes the Rose Bowl Football Classic in Pasadena, California, and they are used in considerable numbers in parades and fiestas throughout the nation. Some Tennessee Walking Horses are of Palomino coloring and make ideal parade horses, being heavy enough to carry the tons of silver that ornament both rider and horse; and although there has never been a pure-bred Arabian that was a Palomino, nor a Thorobred for that matter, many Palominos have been produced that carry a predominance of either Arabian or Thorobred blood. Some of the flashiest Palominos, although seldom large enough for parade animals, are of American Saddle Horse blood, and any number of Quarter Horses are Palominos.

To state (and some people do) that Palominos are "of good disposition," are "sound," are "easy gaited" is, of course, gross foolishness to the extreme degree. It would be just as foolish to state that all black dogs are excellent retrievers, or that all liver and white dogs are top-notch pointers. Individuals of Palomino color may be all the things that are claimed for them, or they may be the exact opposite. In other words, color never made a horse, nor did it ever unmake one.

There has been much talk of late to attempt standardization of the Palomino into, at least, a type if not a breed. It is our thought that the Golden Horse will never amount to much as a "breed" until a determined effort is made by breeders to concentrate a little more on type and conformation, while at the same time maintaining the golden color, if that is their wish. This can be done. The Quarter Horse people have to a considerable extent been able to produce a type, and the Palomino may one day be a recognized breed after enough selective breeding for type has been carried out. At the present time the practice of breeding any animal that shows the "proper" color is doing much to hurt the Palomino. Ruthless elimination of poor breeding stock, regardless of excellence of color, must be practiced. Until this is done the word *Palomino* must indicate a color, not a type, and certainly not a breed.

THE ALBINO HORSE

The Albino horse is a classic example of a "color breed" that has made great strides in the development of standard color in a short period of years. Developed mainly in Nebraska, the Albino is proof that "like begets like" and although breeding of white horses as such was not undertaken until 1918 by C. R. and H. B. Thompson of Swan Lake, Nebraska, Albinos today breed nearly 100 per cent white and are usually of a reasonably standard type. They vary from 15 to 16 hands and weigh from 1000 to 1200 pounds. They are used almost exclusively as parade horses and have been used in the establishment of drill teams that have performed at horse shows, parades and rodeos.

They are, in reality, not a true Albino, for they do not have the pink eye. Usually the eye is brown, although some have a "glass eye," a glassy light blue orb. They are of pink skin and are born white in contrast to white Percherons who are born black.

They make good stock horses, and inasmuch as the breed was developed in two or three localities they are much more uniform in conformation than are horses of the other "color breeds." They closely resemble the Morgan in type and they are of good disposition, easy to train and handsome to the eye. The Morgan blood that they carry has had much to do with their disposition and type and for those who like white horses, the Albino very well serves the purpose.

THE APPALOOSA

The Appaloosa, so states the Appaloosa Horse Club (they also register Appaloosa horses as a breed), are "Colorful enough for a parade; easy riding enough to ride all day; sensible enough for young folks or Grandma; intelligent enough to cut a cow and fast enough to catch a calf." In answer to which we feel it is necessary to say both yes and no.

Here again we have neither type nor breed, but color. Here again, as in all "color breeds," we have some of the best and some of the worst examples of horseflesh imaginable. Just because a horse has colored spots on the croup, a great deal of white in the eye, together with a speckled skin (as does the Appaloosa), it does not make him either exceptionally good or, for that matter, exceptionally bad. Here again, as in the case of the Palomino, many animals have been retained for breeding purposes that conform with the color combination desired but would never have been considered good enough to have been kept as breeders by any other breed. Yet there are some very good Appaloosa as there are very good browns, bays, blacks, or what have you, among Thorobreds. Color, once again, does not make the horse.

The Appaloosa, also known as the Indian Pony, is a descendant of the Spanish horse of Western America and was developed on the Pine Ridge Indian Reservation of South Dakota. They are very prepotent and many Appaloosa stallions readily stamp their pattern of colored spots on their foals regardless of the coloring of the mare. They have been developed into excellent stock horses and, as has been pointed out, are useful as parade animals. They are desirable on Western dude ranches (for the Eastern dude, for some unexplainable reason, seems to associate good horses with color), and many of them have found

77

This appealing Appaloosa mare and foal show good examples of the spotted hind quarters so characteristic of the breed.

Fine six-year-old Appaloosa. The Appaloosa, descendant of the Indian Pony, is traced to the Spanish Horse and makes a wonderful working cow-pony.

their way to rodeo arenas as perfectly acceptable calf-roping and bull-dogging ponies.

*   *   *   *   *

In addition to the above Western types and breeds, there are many lesser types popular in the West: the Colorado Ranger (the result of crossing Arabian stallions onto native mares), the Pinto Horse, also derived from the Indian Pony but being spotted all over rather than merely over the croup as in the Appaloosa, and several combinations of the above and other types. Then, too, one must not forget the Western horse of unknown breeding; that tough little fellow who carries his master over the roughest of terrain day after day, who may not be as handsome as some of his more illustrious cousins, but has nevertheless been a major factor in the development of the Western country as well as the Western horse.

CHAPTER III

HORSE BREEDING

To BREED or not to breed, that is the question. Most horsemen agree that the greatest thrill attainable from their equine cousins is derived from the riding, showing, or racing of animals that have been bred, trained and shown by the owner. Yet regardless of breed or type, several factors should be considered before jumping into the breeding business, even on a small scale.

First, let us establish the fact that it is invariably cheaper to buy a young animal that is ready for training than it is to start wih the mare and stallion and to raise a foal. In addition to the monetary consideration, time is an important factor. Even if we should have a mare on hand during the breeding season it must be remembered that the gestation period of the horse is eleven months, and so from breeding to breaking as a three-year-old we have an elapsed time of four years before we can expect to do very much with our youngster.

If we are to breed we must be prepared to expend funds for (1) stallion fees, (2) maintenance of the mare during her elevenmonth gestation period, plus her board during the suckling year, (3) maintenance of the foal from the time of birth until his three-year-old form is reached. It is impossible to indicate even the cost of the above.

Stud fees vary from $25 to $5000 depending on the stallion used and the breed involved. Many American Saddle Horse stallions of champion caliber command high fees and those asked by some Thorobred stallion owners are astronomical.

As to maintenance cost for both mare and foal, these figures will also vary greatly depending on local conditions. Should we be fortunate enough to own our own farm and produce much of our hay and grains, this cost will be considerably less than for those who find it necessary to pay high board bills for both mare and offspring. One lady of our acquaintance paid a high stud fee to breed her Thorobred hunter to, of all things, a Quarter Horse stallion and paid board bills for both mare and offspring. The result was a worthless three-year-old in which she had invested $3500 and which was eventually sold to the dog-food people for three cents per pound. How much better off this little lady would have been had she gone to the open market and purchased a "made" horse or a youngster ready for training, either of which she could have had for a fraction of the $3500.

The owner of the one- or two-horse stable must also be warned of the "percentages" involved. Every inside straight does not fill, and percentage-wise every mare that is bred does not necessarily conceive, and many that do produce foals of less than questionable value. Any operator of a commercial establishment (who has reached a degree of honesty in the cool of the evening) will confess that the percentage of usable horses produced on his farm is surprisingly small, that he produces four or five mediocre animals for every one of exceptional merit. And so, if our operation is confined to one or two mares, we must be prepared for some disappointments, and the amateur stud farm operator may just as well be cognizant of this hazard. Conversely, countless top-flight horses have been produced by one or two mare stables, and if financial conditions are such that success is not required in every instance, then the amateur is urged to go ahead with an intelligent breeding program.

Even under most ideal of breeding and training conditions, exceptionally finished horses for any purpose are rare enough and are nearly always the result of careful breeding plans. This holds true regardless of size of farm, of number of mares bred, or of the number of stallions available. In this work we may often sound as though we were writing exclusively for the large professional stud farm owner. This is far from true, for the information we are offering may be considerably modified to make it applicable to any manner of breeding venture regardless of scope or location. As to the actual selection of breeding stock, certainly the choice of sire is of primary importance, yet even more imperative is the mare's side of the pedigree, for we must agree with the Bedouin theory that the mare is responsible for at least 60 per cent of the quality of the foal.

THE BROODMARE

Some authorities speak of the ideal broodmare as being "a good milker," "long of neck and shoulder," "big in the barrel, deep chested," or a combination of these and countless like remarks—all true. Yet the breeder will do well to go considerably deeper into the subject before attempting the selection of the broodmare. Obviously, points of conformation are important, yet the type of animal that we wish to produce will have much to do with our choice of mares.

"We breed the best to the best and hope for the best," is an age-old maxim of breeders of all livestock, with the possible exception of the human race. A mare that has been a good performer, either in the show ring or on the track, is naturally more desirable as a broodmare prospect, but merely because she could win in Madison Square Garden or win a matron stakes at Belmont, does not necessarily mean that she can produce winners. Many of our most successful race horses are the foals of unraced dams, and many a champion hunter traces his dam to a female who never saw a fence. Yet, playing the percentages again, a good performer has a better chance of producing a champion than the untried mare.

To deal in generalities, the ideal broodmare is one who most perfectly possesses the desirable conformation of her breed. If we are attempting to produce hunters suitable for the show ring, the mare should stand at least 16 hands at the withers and be either a Thorobred or at least Thorobred type. She should (as should all good mares regardless of breed) "milk like a Guernsey" so that her foal will have a good start in life. She should possess the all-important "hunter disposition," for this is a quality so very often transmitted to the foal. Such a mare, when bred to a desirable stallion, is then ready for the all-important test—can she produce outstanding progeny.

Obviously, in such a risky business, the breeding of mares that have even the slightest defects (except those that may have been the result of physical injury) is hazardous, yet the "proof of the pudding is in the eating," and the test of the broodmare can lie only in what she can produce. Consequently, the safest method of selection lies in the examination of her foals as well as herself. While it should not be difficult to see that this might prove an expensive standard by which to judge and purchase mares, for the proven producer is naturally far more valuable than the unproven and is seldom for sale, it will insure against disappointment.

THE STALLION

As has been pointed out, the mare is responsible for at least 60 per cent of the foal. True enough when one considers each foal individually; however, when we take into consideration that the average mare will produce four foals in five years, while a stallion will serve upward of forty mares per year, the relative importance becomes a matter of simple arithmetic.

Again, as in the selection of all kinds of breeding stock, we are confronted with the aged-old question, "What sort of horses are we attempting to produce?" To which we must now add a second: "What type of mares are available?"

If the situation is such that we have sufficient mares of our own to warrant the purchase and maintenance of a stallion, then the answer to the second question is relatively simple—the mere selection of a horse that we believe will be best suited for our mares. Yet should we have a limited broodmare band and thus are going to depend on other breeders to help defray expense, then the type of mares in our vicinity may influence us considerably. If we are to breed but a very few mares, and suitable stallions are readily available, then the paying of a reasonable stud fee will be the obvious answer.

BREEDING

Assuming that the breeder is supplied with mares which he feels will produce the desired type of foal, and likewise assuming that a suitable stallion is available, then we are ready to undertake a most important part of our venture, the mating of our mares to our stallion.

It would be difficult to overemphasize this all-important phase of the nursery operation, for obviously, if the females do not conceive, the breeder is running a non-profit boarding house for wayward mares. Foal percentages (that ratio between number of mares bred and number of foals produced) will vary greatly. Many factors will influence this percentage—feed conditions—season of year—condition and health of breeding stock; yet the major factor in reproduction is the actual technique of the breeding operations themselves.

There are many aids that the breeder may employ in helping mares to conceive, yet the inexperienced operator should be very wary of tampering with his mares. Well-meaning friends (usually long on conversation, short on experience) will offer countless remedies for the barren mare, yet meddling with the reproductive organs, especially the practice of "opening," is extremely dangerous. As one of our better veterinarians points out, "If horsemen would leave nature alone, if they would interfere less, there would be a higher percentage of foals raised to maturity, and death loss of both mares and foals would diminish."

We are not going to argue that sanitation is not important; it is. However, the breeder will do well to closely scrutinize many of the so-called "sanitary" precautions encountered on some breeding farms. The insertion of the groom's hand—supposedly to "clean" the mare— the flushing out of the vagina, often cause transmission of disease, if not actual physical injury. If for any reason it becomes necessary for the reproductive organs of the mare to be examined, should the mare fail to conceive, or should drainage become evident from the uterus, a competent veterinarian should be summoned, for this is no place for the bungling hand of the enthusiastic amateur.

Our experience has taught us that the most successful manner of operating an equine nursery is to duplicate, as closely as practical, the natural habitat of the horse. Mares and stallions should be kept in a hardy, healthy condition, and if this is accomplished many of the problems concerning conception will be eliminated.

On farms where winters are not too severe (minimum of zero degrees F.) mares are permitted to run in large pastures the year around, with supplementary feeding during cold, snowy months, the only exception being those aged mares that are maintained in paddocks and barned during severe weather. Many breeders feel that, no matter how clean stables are kept, barns are breeding places of disease and are therefore used as seldom as possible.

Stallions should be stabled in roomy box stalls with doors leading to paddocks never closed, barns never heated. They should be exercised every second day under saddle or to the cart (about five miles at a walk or jog) and should be limited to six mares per week. It is customary to stand stallions for the breeding season from February to July, and they are fed six quarts of grain three times daily during the breeding season, twice daily for the remainder of the year, and are never permitted to grow soft and fat. Grains available will have much to do with concentrates fed; a satisfactory ration is five parts rolled oats, three parts rolled barley, two parts wheat bran, one part linseed meal, with the addition of a small amount of cracked corn during exceptionally cold weather.

Good quality timothy or oat hay is kept before the horse at all times, and if the paddock does not afford ample green grass, a small forkful of alfalfa hay may be added to the ration.

Of all the many ramifications influencing foal percentages, perhaps the most paramount is that the mare be taken to the stallion "in season." Should any doubt exist concerning her being "in," it is advisable to pass her rather than to breed her under questionable circumstance. Here again the breeder is confronted with the problem governed by the individual behavior of each mare. Some females, when brought into the company of the stallion (to be tried) will show definite interest in the horse; others are more timid and often take considerable time to indicate if they are in breeding condition.

No set hard-and-fast rules can be offered concerning the actual technique of breeding. Some mares are natural stallion fighters and must be hobbled, yet hobbles, as the twitch, should not be used except as a last resort, for the mare will have a much greater chance of conception if she is completely relaxed. The mare should be kept as quiet as possible, her halter held by a man who is known to her. The stallion should be kept well in hand and disciplined in the event that he attempts to rush the mare or to frighten her by striking, biting and in any manner giving an obnoxious performance. The men in the breeding shed or paddock should speak softly, and the mare should be permitted to see her foal kept in a small stall in one corner of the shed—in sight of the mare but out of harm's way.

The stallion is made to walk to the mare quietly, mount on order and to act the gentleman throughout. Stallions, when out of hand, are apt to attempt to show their authority. For this there is no excuse, and if he is permitted to act outrageously, it's time to change stallion grooms.

Mares' tails are bandaged during breeding to insure against interference and injury to both mare and stallion by loose tail hairs, and the *external* genitals of the mare are washed with pure Castile soap. This washing is done so as to remove any organic matter that may be present, and to eliminate all risks of surface infection to both mare and horse.

After the mare is bred the stallion is immediately returned to his stall, the mare walked (in the company of her foal should she have one) for at least fifteen minutes, the groom discouraging her from urinating. Without further delay her tail bandage is removed and she is turned onto pasture undisturbed for fourteen days. On the fourteenth day she is brought in and again introduced to the stallion and "tried." Heat periods vary greatly with individual mares, yet most operators agree that the mare should be brought to the stallion every second day, beginning with the fourteenth and ending with the twenty-sixth.

Should the mare show symptoms of being in season (relaxing of the external genitals, frequent urination, or teasing other mares or geldings) she should be returned to the stallion and if necessary be rebred. If, on the other hand, she shows none of these indications, trials are continued twice weekly for the balance of the breeding season.

If these trials are conducted as described above, 85 per cent to 90 per cent of mares that have refused the stallion can safely be considered in foal, nevertheless the beginner must realize that there will always be a small percentage of mares who, although they display little interest in the stallion, have still not conceived. Here is a case for a competent veterinarian who will be able either to diagnose and treat the difficulty or to pronounce the mare a hopelessly barren female.

THE FOAL

Now that the mare is with foal, her previous offspring weaned, and having been wintered outdoors and being in good, thrifty condition, she is watched very closely for the first signs of impending parturition. Thirty days before she is due to foal—311 days after her last breeding—the mare is brought to the foaling barn and assigned a roomy stall (at least 14 x 14 feet) which is to be her home until a week after foaling.

She is allowed to self-exercise in a small paddock adjacent to the foaling barn during the warm hours, and those that refuse to move about voluntarily are walked for thirty minutes each morning. Care must be exercised to see that animals are not warmed up too much and that they are removed to their stalls before the cool of winter evening.

Eminent signs of impending parturition are not always standard. Mares are individuals and must be treated as such. Most will secrete a waxlike substance from the teat for a period ranging from twelve hours to three days before going into labor. This wax, the result of first milk forced from the teat, is generally a dependable guide; yet some mares do not have wax at any time, and therefore the beginner must not be too surprised if the mare prepares to foal without this telltale sign.

As actual foaling approaches (perhaps an hour or two before labor begins) most mares will start circling about their stalls. Some break out in perspiration about the head and shoulders, while others will give little indication of a forthcoming blessed event. One old mare that has been in our family for many years gives hardly any warning. Instead, she merely lies down, stretches out flat on her side and quietly gives birth with no more fuss than a deep sigh. To help matters she has produced one outstanding foal after another.

The beginner must be warned that nature, in her infinite wisdom, knows far more about foaling than does the average man, and nature should be given her chance. Even experienced stud farm operators often make the mistake of becoming overanxious, of insisting upon helping the mare during foaling when no help is indicated.

Sanitation during foaling is of vast importance, for many equine diseases are contracted during and immediately following parturition. Stalls must be scrupulously clean and a generous supply of clean straw bedding free from chaff must be supplied.

Bandaging of the mare's tail previous to parturition to prevent hairs interfering or becoming matted is recommended, and it is advisable to have someone of practical experience present. Some mares, especially those of advanced years, will take so much time in foaling as to become exasperating. They will lie down, rise, walk around the stall, sniff at the man in attendance, and lie down again. They may bite at their flanks, give a performance of great pain, and then, when the attendant is thoroughly frightened and positive that something is drastically wrong, they will calmly stretch out and without further ado have their foal. Yet, should the mare labor for an hour or more without result, then the operator has just cause for concern.

The foal at birth. Note the sterile oilcloth "drop cloth." Here sanitation is of first importance, and the wise nursery operator will do everything to maintain such sanitation.

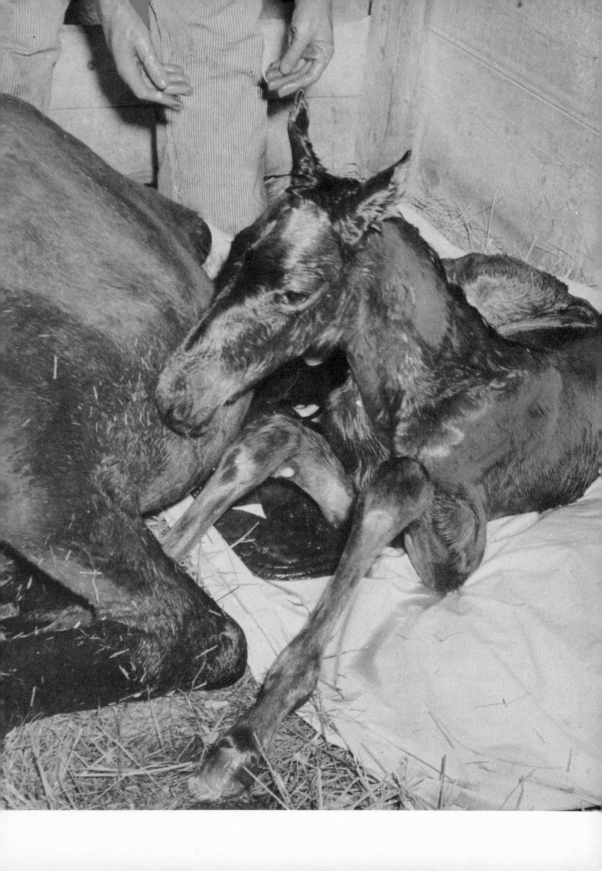

When the mare does foal, the front feet emerge first, one slightly in advance of the other, with the head between the forelegs. When this much of the normally presented foal makes its appearance the operator may justly relax for the speculative chances of impending difficulty are greatly reduced. If but one foot appears followed by the head, it will be necessary to push the foal back gently into the vagina, to reach in (after disinfecting the hands or while wearing sterile rubber gloves) and secure the second foot—which is possibly doubled back over the head and neck—and then, having straightened out the foal, permit the mare to continue for a time unassisted. Should the attendant find it necessary to help the mare by applying actual pressure, a pull downwards, directly towards the mare's hind feet, is advisable. One should remember never to pull unless the mare is straining, for if the operator does not synchronize with the mare's labors, serious consequences may result. Should the foal be presented backward, should it appear deformed in any manner, or if the mare shows unmistable weakness from prolonged straining, a veterinarian should be summoned at once.

Once born, the foal should be permitted to rise to his feet unassisted, and normal foals will, after several attempts, manage to rise and to nurse within the first hour of life. Weak foals, or those that are born of obstinate mares, are assisted to the teat, yet no assistance should be offered unless absolutely necessary to preserve the foal's life.

After the foal has nursed for the first time, all soiled bedding is removed, the placenta taken away to be burned or buried, and fresh straw spread. A small dose (about one ounce) of castor oil is often given to the foal immediately after its first nursing, and if any sign of constipation is evident the posterior bowel is cleaned out with a finger that has been first carefully washed and coated with vaseline.

For the first thirty-six hours the mare and foal are confined to the foaling stall, and the mare is supplied with lukewarm water or gruel if climatic conditions warrant. At the end of this period, weather again permitting, they should be turned out onto a small, wind-protected court during the warm sunlight hours. The foal is vaccinated against navel ill at about three days, and then, if all is progressing swimmingly, if he is nursing well, and has reached the age of one week without incident, the mare and foal are turned out to pasture with the remainder of the broodmare band.

The average foal will start nibbling grain at about nine to fifteen days. At the start, he should be permitted to eat with his dam; then, as his appetite increases, the mare is tied adjacent to her feed box, the foal given one of his own. His ration will be influenced by feeds available, a rolled oat and wheat bran mixture being ideal. Should the youngster be produced during the winter (and there is little if any grass available) a small amount of alfalfa hay may be fed along with timothy or oat hay.

Foals should be handled as quickly as possible after birth, and this handling should be continued to assure gentleness and confidence in man. Halter breaking should be an accomplished fact during the first thirty to sixty days, and the youngster should be led about at regular intervals throughout the foal year.

Halter breaking, the first lesson the foal will be expected to learn, is of vast importance, for what horseman has not at one time or another encountered a mature horse that balks, leads badly, or is touchy about the head or ears. Most of these faults are due to a careless start or complete neglect on the part of the original trainer.

In the beginning, a stout colt halter is adjusted to the foal and he is taken to a small exercise pen or corral in the company of his dam. At first he is permitted to follow his mother, but as he becomes accustomed to the man at his head, as he stops fighting the lead shank, he is asked to walk away from the mare. The beginner will soon learn that little is gained by fighting the foal—or in attempting to rush the training. Time now is of little importance, and a few additional minutes spent during the first few lessons will pay tremendous dividends in later training phases.

After foals have been broken to lead they may be permitted to carry a lightweight halter throughout their foal winter, a short strap (about fourteen inches long) being snapped into the halter ring. When mares and foals are brought in to be fed the attendant may catch each foal by the short shank and lead them about the stall. This simple routine takes but a few minutes daily and does much for the gentling process.

All youngsters should have their feet rasped every thirty days, and to be certain that this all-important function is not overlooked, many nursery operators set aside the first few days of each month for this work. As the wall of the hoof grows rapidly (especially if the breeding band is running on soft rather than rocky terrain) frequent trimming is necessary to prevent splitting of the hoof shell. The heels should be kept level, and although a rasp and knife are all the equipment necessary for the very young, a light pair of hoof nippers will be handy when the foal reaches six months.

Many foals are born that appear as though they will never stand squarely on their feet; yet one must not be too hasty to pass judgment. Let us give the foal a chance, let us not be too critical for the first thirty days. Pasterns that at first appear too long, or with too much slope, often straighten out. Foals that appear "sprung" at the knees often make a complete recovery, while feet that appear too long and force the foal to "rock" on his hind legs usually adjust themselves.

When a month of age is reached and the foal still does not stand squarely on his four feet, careful trimming of the hoofs often will result in either complete rectification of this condition, or at least a correction to a considerable degree will be accomplished.

It is impossible to overemphasize the care of the feet, the horse's "second heart." A horse with poor, shelly feet is no horse at all, and the time to start hoof care is at thirty days of age and never thereafter can the vigilance be relaxed. While experienced horseshoers have accomplished wonders by diligent care of the feet, the amateur must be wary of making corrections in the hope of improving or minimizing hoof and leg defects. Many so-called "sore shoulders" are traceable to hoof difficulties usually caused by neglect in early life.

As weaning time approaches, with the foal consuming three to four quarts of mixed grain daily, the beginner will do well to disregard much of the advice that has been offered concerning weaning. Some authorities come out with the bold-faced statement that foals should be weaned at five months; others are as sure that it should be six, some insist on seven. All right. All wrong.

Weaning, like so much equine, is a matter of individuality. Some foals attain enough size and are eating well enough to warrant weaning at five months. Others should not be weaned as long as the mare is capable of producing milk. Condition of the mare will be another determining factor. Aged mares, or mares that have produced exceptionally promising foals, may not make a full recovery by the time the next foal is produced, and therefore must have a longer rest between lactations— their foals weaned earlier than those of younger mares of less value.

The first consideration then is the physical condition of the foal; second, the condition of the mare; and third, the value of the mare in proportion to the value of the foal. Experience alone can determine degree of "condition" in a horse; however, it takes no expert to ascertain the lack of this quality. Other than a good coating of flesh, the state of the hair is an excellent condition guide. Hair that does not lie down well, that lacks luster, is a sure indication of poor condition. Dullness of the eye is another sure sign that weight is being lost and the general behavior of the animal is important to observe. The value of the foal in proportion to the worth of the mare will depend on the individuals involved and calls for an experienced eye.

As weaning time approaches some nurseries add dry skim milk to the foal ration, gradually increasing the skim milk content from a quarter pound to from one to two pounds daily at time of weaning. It is felt that this dry skim milk not only partially replaces the mare's milk, but also that its high mineral content makes this a highly valuable practice.

After the male foal has been weaned, he should be studied with altering in mind. All males must be altered unless they show unmistakable signs of becoming outstanding individuals, and consequently candidates for the stud. Here again we must caution against taking too literally advice concerning the "proper" age for altering. Weanlings that begin to thicken in the neck and develop early masculinity should be altered before their yearling year; those that are slower in development, are more inclined toward the feminine type, should be left untouched until such time as they do develop sufficiently. The practice of altering all weanlings at the same time—of fixing an arbitrary date for this important operation—is therefore not to be recommended, and the breeder will do well to study each colt as an individual.

For the balance of the foal year (after weaning) foals do little but eat, sleep and play. True, they are handled as often as time will permit, but with the exception of fall worming and hoof care, they should be undisturbed and permitted to do much as they please.

Except for the "hot house" candidates for the Saratoga and other yearling sales that are pampered and overfed to give them unwarranted size, weanlings are not necessarily stabled. Instead they run on small pastures, they're fed their grain ration in common bunks and are given all the hay they will clean up. In colder climates they may have access to sheds open to the south, but they are not blanketed nor often groomed. Instead, they are permitted to grow long healthy coats and allowed to run free until their first serious schooling is undertaken. Heaven knows their days of complete freedom will be short enough, for very soon it will be necessary to put them into intensified training and their romping days will be over.

CHAPTER IV

HORSE TRAINING

ALMOST anyone who can read, follow simple directions, has an observant eye and can get around in a wheel chair can be a success in a horse-breeding program. Not so when it comes to training. It is true that diligent study, coupled with a degree of natural ability can transform a rank amateur into at least a passable trainer. Working as an assistant to a successful trainer is also invaluable for the beginner; yet, unfortunately for the tyro, top-flight trainers—the producers of outstanding horses regardless of breed or type—are born, not made.

This does not necessarily imply that all exceptional horses are the product of a full-time professional—far from it. Many of the finest performers of both show ring and field are the result of diligent amateur training, for often the nonprofessional will be able to devote his undivided attention to one or two horses, while the large-scale training master is handicapped with an excessive number of animals, his time thinly spread among a host of youngsters.

Contrary to the romantic fictions of *Black Beauty, Kilgour's Mare* and the like, the horse holds a rather low position in the intelligence scale of the animal kingdom. Consequently, patience and more patience is required for their schooling. Instruction must be repeated over and over for successful results. Many inexperienced trainers become exasperated (and understandably so) with the animal's stupidity, lose their patience and very often their heads. Result: a spoiled horse.

Next to patience, self-confidence in the trainer is perhaps the most important ingredient. Many believe that the horse can smell fear in the man. This we wonder about, yet we have all known horses who perform well when handled by a competent horseman only to completely fall apart when ridden by a fearful novice. Can this highly necessary confidence be developed? Certainly. Should the tyro be careful and not overmatch himself early in his career; should he be properly guided and serve his apprenticeship with horses under the intelligent guidance of someone smart enough not to start him off on a spoiled outlaw, then this confidence can be developed to a marked degree. Conversely, many a promising young horseman has been completely ruined by the stupidity of some well-meaning friend who overmounts him, gets him tossed about and completely obliterates whatever confidence he may have possessed. For this rider, the wooden horse of the merry-go-round will be horse enough.

TRAINING THE YOUNG HORSE

There are many differences of opinion concerning the "proper" age to undertake the training of the horse. Custom, location, time available and practicability are deciding factors, and yet the purpose to which the horse is destined will in most instances be the final and deciding factor.

Obviously, if our youngster is destined for the track—if he is to be ready to go as a two-year-old, little time can be lost. If, instead, our baby is to wind up leading the Fiesta of Roses Parade and will be required to learn little beyond good head and tail carriage and the ability to carry a few hundred pounds of silver and *caballero* without falling on his face, perhaps this little fellow may be permitted to run wild until he is a four-year-old and then "broken out" in the Western manner rather than trained as would be necessary in the case of the American Saddle Horse, a show hunter or a light harness animal.

Time available will, of course, be a determining factor. Should we have from five to ten hours spread throughout the week to devote to our young animal, fine and good. But, if we must keep brushing our Grey Flannel Suit and have but limited time away from the market place, then perhaps we will have to forgo many of the frills of early training. We feel that we are right when we insist that the earlier training is undertaken the better regardless of breed or type. With this thought in mind we will outline a somewhat detailed training program, leaving to the reader the editing of the material to fit his particular conditions.

*　*　*　*　*

Having reached fourteen to fifteen months of age, the yearling should be brought in from pasture and assigned a stall. He will not be asked to perform great feats during this, his second year, yet his training will do much to keep him gentle, to maintain growth through proper feeding together with considerable supervised exercise.

Time permitting, he should be groomed daily, particular care given to the ears and head so that he will not object to the application of the headstall, and hoofs should be "picked out" after each grooming. Actual schooling should not be undertaken until the youngster has become accustomed to being stabled, to being tied in his stall and to having men working about him.

First bridling of the yearling is of lifelong importance. Much of the joy of riding is derived from the animal with a sensitive mouth—the horse that works willingly on a loose rein, the horse that responds instantly to light pressure from the hands. Nothing is worse than the "lunkhead": that animal that pulls the arms from the rider's sockets. Heavier and more severe bits are often employed to try to correct this fault until the poor beast has everything in his mouth but the kitchen stove and still he is anything but a pleasure to behold, let alone ride.

At the beginning a leather-covered bar-bit is ideal. The bit is placed in the mouth (the headstall not drawn too tightly) and the yearling permitted to mouth the bit while standing in the stall for half hour periods. This is continued a number of times until he becomes accustomed to the strange feeling of something solid between the teeth and no longer attempts to dislodge it. Next, a surcingle (a four-inch-wide leather band with two rein loops) is fitted to him and gradually pulled up snug about his middle.

Once accustomed to bit and surcingle, he is taken to a small stoutly fenced enclosure (50 x 50 feet is perfect) for his first lesson. At the start two persons should work with the colt; the assistant walking at his headstall, the trainer following along behind with the lines. This is continued until such time as the yearling becomes accustomed to the slapping of the lines against his back and flanks and until he reacts to slight pressure on the bit. Until the trainer is completely certain that he has the young animal under full control, he should never be permitted to work without the man at his head.

This hand driving is continued for at least ten lessons of about one-half hour each, with standing and backing gradually added to walking and turning. Soon the youngster will learn to respond to the commands of the trainer and the man with the lines will soon be able to stand in the center of the enclosure working the colt around him in circles.

The next step, driving to the breaking cart, brings up still another controversy in a field fraught with controversy. We have, for many years, driven all manner of young horses with what we consider good results. Yet for every trainer who agrees with us that driving horses

Driving the yearling to the long lines. This will do much to gentle the youngster as well as to start the all-important development of the rein.

The dumb jockey is an ideal training device for the young horse. The double lines from the bridle to the arms of the "jockey" may be adjusted to any length so that the neck may be flexed to the desires of the trainer.

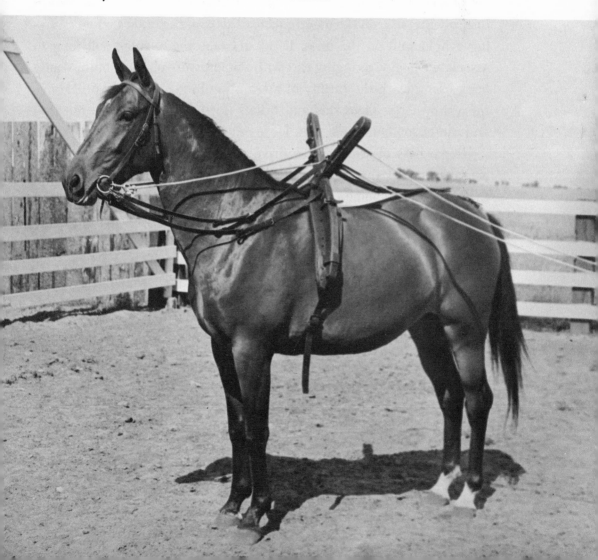

destined for the saddle is beneficial, up will pop at least one other first-class horseman who will insist that the driving of saddle horses is a waste of time and sometimes downright harmful. They insist that many a youngster has had his mouth ruined by early driving, stating that the average driver is prone to tug on the lines, the only control he has over the animal.

Of course the critics are right. Right as rain when they refer to the old-style breaking cart. We have designed a cart that removes this objectionable feature for our cart is equipped with brakes. The brakes are attached so that each wheel brakes individually, much in the manner of a tractor. Should the youngster decide to bolt, it is not necessary to apply pressure on the mouth; instead slap on the brakes while applying a light pull on the lines. It doesn't take the average colt long to associate a heavy, dragging cart with rein pressure on the mouth; young horses soon learn the futility of attempting to get away. As quickly as the youngster realizes this and quiets down, the brakes are released and the lesson continued on a loose rein.

Regardless of whether we drive the saddle candidate or not, the actual fitting of the saddle to the horse's back cannot be undertaken too early in life. Some trainers tell us that they never saddle short of a two-year-old, others insist on waiting until the three-year-old form. Us? We like to saddle the youngster as a long yearling. We are not too large ourselves, and we like to work with young horses, horses in whom we have instilled confidence. We work on the same principle as when teaching our children to swim almost before they can walk—certainly long before they develop fear of water.

Our yearling is first fitted to saddle without stirrups and with a loose girth. He is then allowed to stand tied in his stall for from fifteen to thirty minutes at a time. As he becomes accustomed to the feel of the saddle, the girth is taken up until he is willing to stand quietly as it is drawn snug. Next, stirrups are added and he is removed to the training enclosure where he is lunged with stirrups flopping.

Size of the young horse will have much to do with age of mounting. Big, raw-boned youngsters may be mounted in their yearling year; light-boned, delicate colts should wait until their two-year-old form before being asked to carry weight. When mounting is undertaken a light rider (less than one hundred pounds) of either sex (for often a girl is as handy at this stage as a boy) is set up while the colt stands in his stall with a man at his head. These mountings are repeated each day for at least a week, the lesson never prolonged over a fifteen-minute period. The boy (or girl) should mount and dismount often during this period, and the practice should be repeated over and over again until the colt has become thoroughly accustomed to this stepping on and off.

Now that the colt is no longer bothered by weight on his back, a hackamore (a bitless headstall that depends on nostril rather than mouth pressure, and therefore does not invite a spoiled mouth) replaces the leather-covered bit that had been used in driving, and the animal is taken to the small training area.

A man should be kept at the colt's head for at least the first few lessons to lead the youngster about in circles and even though the young horse gives every indication that he is prepared to behave, the man should stay at his head until all nervousness has vanished. Many times the colt will appear trustworthy, yet when turned loose and realizing that he has a free head, he may become playful causing injury to himself or to his rider. Should he "break up," his training will be greatly retarded. A horse that is never permitted to buck will seldom learn, for bucking, like any other horse accomplishment, must be learned and developed.

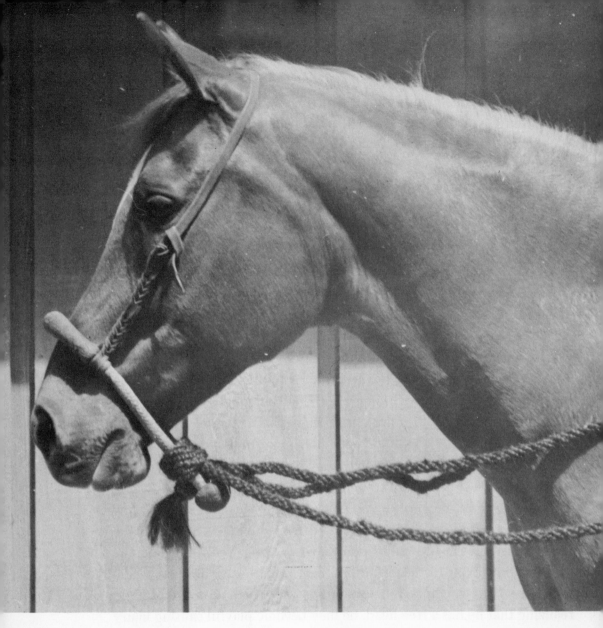

The hackamore (a bitless headstall that depends on nostril rather than mouth pressure) is an ideal starter for the young horse. Here there is little chance of inviting a spoiled mouth and some of our best reined horses are the result of the hackamore.

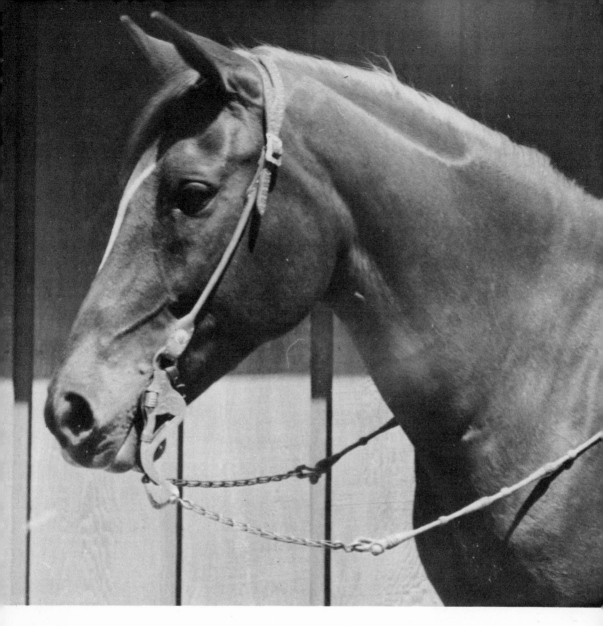

The half-breed bit is often the second step in bridling. Here the youngster may play with the "roller" and a soft chin strap is used rather than a chain curb.

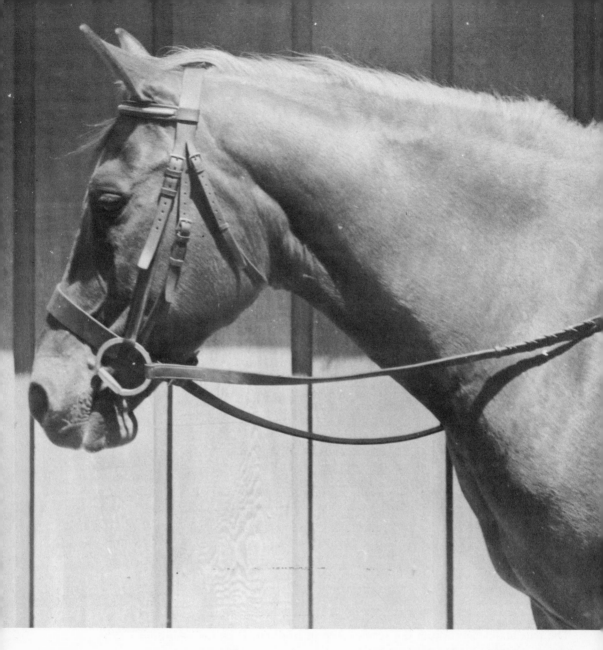

Here the hunter snaffle is used in place of the half-breed. For those animals destined for the hunting field we need go no further, for a well-schooled animal should work well with nothing more severe than the snaffle.

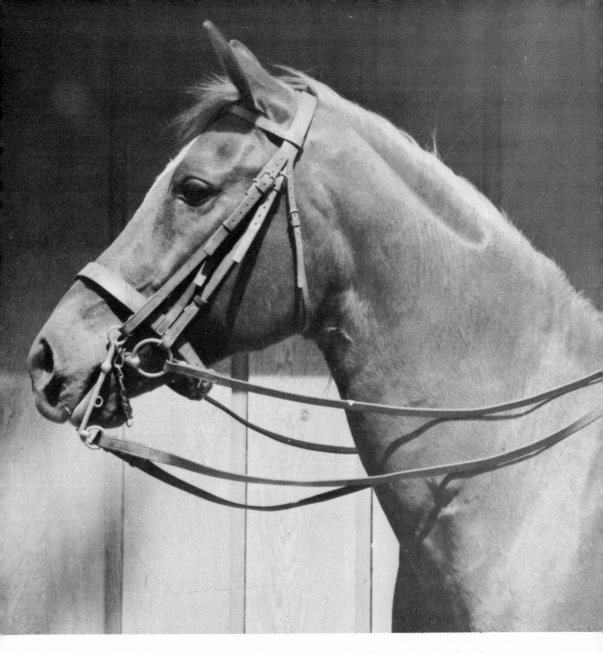

The final step—the full English double bridle. This will be the final step for the American Saddle Horse and other breeds where the full bridle is used.

When one remembers that the horse does not reach maturity until from five to six years of age, it becomes immediately understandable that "overdoing" is far more detrimental than "underdoing." Here is no place for the impatient; here we have little sympathy for the man in a hurry. Walk the colt, walk him and walk him again until he will turn, figure eight, and behave quietly. Insist that he stand perfectly still when being mounted. Should he move, the rider should take his foot from the stirrup and try again. Keep stepping down and eventually the colt will assimilate the general idea that he must stand. Speak to the horse, speak in a quiet but authoritative voice: "Stand!" "Walk!" "Stop!" etc. The colt will soon become accustomed to the inflection of your voice and learn to obey. The animal that has been driven to the long lines will more readily learn to obey and less time will be required for this phase of training than for those that have not had the advantage of having been driven.

Regardless of what age we undertake actual saddle training, we will gradually progress from the walk to the trot; from the trot to the gallop, and from the gallop to the canter. All this will take months—in some instances perhaps years—but all the while the gentling process is being carried on. Colts are groomed as before, feet "picked out," trimmed and, when necessary, shod.

*   *   *   *   *

Up to this point our training schedule is for all kinds of young saddle horses regardless of breed or type. We should now have reached that admirable stage of life where our youngster is green, but gently broken. He should be driving well to the cart, completely gentle under saddle and now ready for the specialized training that will equip him for his eventual job of work.

As the young hunter prospect reaches the point where he is completely trustworthy under saddle, he may be introduced to the Hitchcock pen. This pen, developed on our Eastern seaboard, is the answer to the hunter trainer's prayers. Construction may be of many kinds of material from the elaborate, costing thousands of dollars, to the most reasonable, made of waste material. In some instances narrow lanes are used with good results, yet the Hitchcock is without peer. The ideal size would be one sixty feet long by thirty wide. The pen is oblong with rounded ends, the outer walls solid and a minimum of seven feet high. On the inside, and about twelve feet from this solid outer wall, a rail three feet high is put in place, so that the interior resembles a miniature racetrack. Any number of jumps in any design may be set up on this track, and the colt always in a "chute" is under complete control and must take the obstacles as he comes to them.

During the first lessons, the orientation course as it were, single bar jumps are used from nine to twenty-four feet apart, and are laid flat on the ground. The youngster is turned into the pen unaccompanied and allowed to sniff about and to examine its contents at his leisure. Once he is acquainted with the pen the single bar jumps are raised to the height of one foot (solid, so that they cannot be knocked down), and the colt is driven around the pen loose and, of course, without rider. This is great sport to most youngsters and the majority will make the circle with little encouragement, flying over the jumps as they come to them; others may require the snap of a buggy whip to persuade them to take the course.

By the time our young hunter is a three-year-old, various types of jumps may be erected in the Hitchcock—the most popular and serviceable, alternating brush and "hogs'-backs." Jumps should be no more than two feet in height at the start and are gradually raised to three

feet six inches as we progress. The use of "hogs'-backs" is of paramount importance. Hunters who have been properly schooled over "hogs'-backs" learn to jump big (take off well back of the jump; land well forward of the obstacle) instead of their counterpart—that horror of horrors of the hunting field—the horse that rushes his fences, comes to almost a complete stop and then crow-hops. In regards to the colt that through sheer laziness runs through the brush jumps instead of clearing them, a piece of inch pipe embedded the full length of the jump and just under the top of the brush will do much to discourage this common and bothersome fault.

When the three-year-old has learned to jump properly while loose and unmounted, he may be returned to the Hitchcock under saddle and mounted by a light rider. At first, jumps should be no higher than two feet and should be solid so that they cannot be knocked down or run through. As the colt progresses, varied types of jumps replace the common single bar that had been used at the beginning and they are raised to from three feet to three feet six inches depending on progress, so that by the time the hunter prospect has reached his three-year-old fall, he is jumping all sorts of obstacles in the confines of the pen.

At this point the trainer must use his judgment as to whether the colt is ready to work over the outside course. If so, he should not be asked to take more than sixteen jumps per week, and ample wings should be provided to keep the colt from running out. As he progresses, a large ring-snaffle bit should replace the hackamore, and the jump wings should be removed so that the "long" three-year-old should be jumping all obstacles (none higher than three feet) and without wings.

The yearling jumping in the Hitchcock Pen. The Hitchcock, built in the manner of a miniature race track with solid outer wall is the ideal training aid for the young hunter prospect. Note that the jumps are adjustable and that they are solid so that they cannot be knocked down.

Now we add a second hunter to our lesson, preferably a quiet, made hunter, to acquaint our prospect with his fellows and to jump in the company of others. If he is destined to hunt in the field rather than to become strictly a show-ring performer, and if he is handling well, he should be introduced to hounds. In most hunting country before the official season begins, young hounds are taken cubbing, and here is an ideal introduction to hunting for our youngster.

The beginning trainer must be warned not to ask the hunter prospect to keep up with the field should the pace become too rapid; but, instead, to drop out or to follow along at a more leisurely pace. He should never be asked to jump much higher than three feet, for we must remember that our young horse is still in the stage of development and vital tendons might easily be strained. Should faults develop in the field, the colt should be returned to the Hitchcock at once and corrections made under strict control before uncorrectable habits are permitted to form.

As a four-year-old, the hunter prospect should be ready for any obstacle up to four feet. By this time he should not require the confinements of the Hitchcock; instead he should be working in a large ring, or better still, in open hunting country. Having been properly schooled over "hogs'-backs," he should be jumping big and he should be jumping all manner of obstacles without wings.

As we gradually make our way to the finished hunter, the trainer should be cautioned against asking too much of the horse and thereby forcing him to sour. As in all schooling of horses, frequent short sessions are far more desirable than longer sessions conducted at longer intervals. Give the hunter plenty of rest, but when he is being worked, insist upon perfection. Should he refuse his jumps take him back to the Hitchcock and teach him, with the whip if necessary, that this just will not do. Should he rush his fences work him in the Hitchcock again with jumps placed either closer together, or on the sharp turns, or both. Always remember to feed regularly, and on schedule, to exercise and school on schedule. Insist on complete and unqualified obedience and you'll come up with a finished hunter of which you may be justly proud.

THE AMERICAN SADDLE HORSE

If we have schooled the American Saddle Horse as outlined under "Training the Young Horse," we are now ready for the specialized training necessary to develop this peacock of the equine world. We are safe in assuming that our candidate has been driven to the breaking cart (for of all the breeds, trainers of Saddlers nearly always start their charges on the cart) or, at the very least, worked to the long lines.

Bitting is of vast importance for the saddler and again we run into many controversial recommendations. Some trainers insist on a gradual change from the hackamore (if it has been used at all) to the bridoon (snaffle) to the double bridle with English curb and snaffle bits—the final bitting goal for all American Saddle Horses. It is universally agreed, however, that if the transition to the double bridle is made quickly, care must be exercised not to tighten the curb strap too suddenly, thus avoiding possible injury to the youngster's mouth during early training. It goes without saying that when the double bridle is used, all pressure should be applied to the snaffle, the curb used only when absolutely necessary and then with great care.

As in the case of all young horses, the Saddler should at first be schooled at the walk and never permitted to break into a trot or gallop. It is during this important stage of training (at least two months of schooling at the walk) that he learns to respond to the bit and to acquire balance, for now that he is being asked to carry the weight of the rider he must adjust himself to a completely new set of balances.

Here, too, he learns to gather himself; to get his hocks under him; to learn to walk with "control" instead of the free, ambling shuffle that he has used all during his free life.

From the walk we progress to the trot, the trot signal the age-old laying of the hand on the youngster's mane halfway from withers to head, with the rider leaning slightly forward in the saddle and, if necessary, encouraging the colt with leg and heel pressure. Trot him for a few minutes; bring him down gently to a halt; walk him for a few minutes; bring him to a halt, and trot again. The Saddler will very quickly associate pressure on his neck with the rider's desire to trot, and we have made great headway in our schooling. Gradually we can ask for more speed at the trot and as the youngster responds, we may let up on hand pressure until he is working at an extended trot and under loose rein which should be our goal at this stage of life.

Having mastered the walk and the trot, both with loose rein, we are ready to take the five-gaited candidate into his distinctive gait, the rack. Here we will separate the men from the boys—the sheep from the goats, for here we will find whether we have a five-gait, or must settle for a three. There are several methods employed by trainers to teach the rack; yet the beginner must be warned that although we will outline what we feel the most sensible and successful method, all American Saddle Horses cannot be brought to perfection in the rack and that all trainers are not infallible in the production of this most difficult gait. Even the most experienced of trainers produce Saddlers that prove mediocre at the rack, much as many a great music master produces soloists that leave much to be desired when they mount the concert stage.

During the first racking lesson, the colt is worked in the training ring and is asked to walk along the outer rail. As he walks, the trainer-rider encourages him to swing his head from side to side by slight give-and-take pressure on one rein, while steadying him with the other. This will eventually produce an ambling gait—progress from the walk, a four-beat gait, to the rack, also a four-beat gait. This ambling gait (the swinging of the head synchronized with the movement of his legs and his entire body for that matter) should be taught for short periods only, perhaps ten minutes per session, and repeated daily for at least a week before attempting to go further.

As we make headway, we may gradually let up on mouth pressure, all the while encouraging the colt to more speed. After all, the Saddler has for countless generations been bred to rack and the willing youngster will soon be performing with a minimum of faults. He should be encouraged, petted, talked to and made to feel that he is accomplishing greatness, which he is, after all, for one so young.

Should he break from the rack to the trot or get completely out-of-hand and try to gallop, he must be brought back to the walk, the entire process taken again from the beginning. As he continues to improve, head swinging can gradually be discouraged by rein pressure, the rider shifting his own weight to assist the young Saddler.

Much has been written about the use of quarter boots, the trimming of feet, and actual shoeing in order to increase action of the Saddler, especially in assisting him to rack. All this is true, for proper foot care and some mechanical aids can do much in the development of the gaited horse. Yet, this is no place for the amateur and often more harm than good is accomplished by forced methods. Here the beginner must seek the advice of a first-rate trainer, and the less said about this sort of thing here the better.

By now we should have the young Saddler proficient in three gaits —the walk, the trot, the rack, and we are ready for the next step in his education, the canter. The canter is, of course, nothing more than the gallop (a natural gait for all horses) under perfect control in the matter of speed and collection.

At the start, the youngster should be taken into a good-sized exercise area and broken into a gallop. This may be accomplished in many ways; the rider leaning well forward while applying leg pressure; or (as some prefer) to lean well back in the saddle while applying heel pressure. Regardless of what method is used, the colt, once into the gait, is permitted to have a good romp for himself, the rider encouraging him in his work and assuring him that this is the desired gait and that the youngster is not misbehaving as he had done when he broke from the trot or rack to the gallop. This same procedure is continued once each day for at least a week, the gallop always being started in the same spot in the exercise area and always from a standing start. The colt very soon associates the geographic location with the rider's desire to gallop—and gallop he will, usually with great pleasure.

Gradually the speed of the gallop is controlled until such time as we have a hand gallop, which in turn we will then convert to a well-controlled canter. Concerning leads, the young animal is taught to lead either right or left by one of two methods: by leg and heel pressure on the opposite side of the desired lead, or by leaning slightly towards the desired lead. Strangely, one method may work well with one individual and be all but worthless with another. But the result must be the same and the horse taught to lead off on either foot. Gradually this signal for the canter should be minimized until it is hardly discernible to the onlooker.

The fifth and final gait for the Saddler is, of course, the slow gait, either the amble, which is nothing more or less than a very slow and controlled rack, or the fox trot which may be defined as the trot performed in a very slow and deliberate manner. The fox trot is often linked to the running walk, and neither it nor the amble is difficult to teach. After all, our young animal has already gone through the ambling business while learning to rack and if we have done a workmanlike job, we have produced at least a passable trot. So the slow gait, no matter which we wish to employ, develops into a matter of patience, diligent work and continued repetition until the gait is mastered.

From here on the trainer is completely on his own. The animal having been gaited, knowing his five gaits, and working each on command, may go just as far as his ability and that of his trainer will permit. He should be worked diligently and often, for long rest periods are always dangerous in any kind of equitation because the animal forgets his lessons and relearning is not easy. So now it's up to the trainer to keep him going and to take him as far along towards proficiency as possible.

THE WESTERN HORSE

When we speak of breaking the Western horse, we indicate a method of breaking not necessarily limited to the horse of the West, or of the Western breeds. Rather we speak of a system of breaking that is applicable to all saddle stock. Many a ten-goal polo pony, a top hunter, or an outstanding American Saddle Horse has been broken in this manner and with excellent results. True, some Eastern and Midwestern trainers deplore some of the more rugged Western practices, yet they must admit that a horse broken in the Western manner by an expert in his field is often superior to that animal trained from colthood by one of less talent and experience. Eastern critics must also admit that the Western method is far less expensive, inasmuch as little if anything is done with the horse until he is a four- or five-year-old; and for the man in a hurry to produce a well-broken saddle animal, it is the indisputable answer.

Louis Cabral of Tres Pinos, California, is such an expert. The proof lies in his development of countless top-flight horses ranging from cutting and roping horses to some of the fanciest trick riding mounts in the country today. Once a top rodeo hand who competed in all manner of events from bronc riding to calf roping, Cabral has retired from arena competition and is now considered the country's leading trick and fancy rider performing in rodeos and fiestas throughout the land. In the off-season he devotes his time to the training of all types of horses and many of the following practices are his, some original, others refinements of techniques used in the West since the days of the Spaniard.

"I like to start with a horse that has never seen a man," Cabral states, "and I never like to touch a horse until he is a four-year-old. By then his bones are hard and set; he's strong enough to take the business, and if he's ever going to have any savvy, he'll have it by then."

Being a four-year-old and never having been handled, halter breaking (the first step) becomes much more interesting than our experience in teaching our suckling colt to lead in the company of his well-trained dam. Now we are working with a mature animal, one that will weigh a thousand pounds rather than the young colt's three hundred, and various force methods may become necessary.

At first the horse is driven into a small catch pen. He is roped and fitted with a stout leather or web halter together with a six-foot neck rope, a ¾ inch soft cotton line that is tied snugly about his neck just behind the ears (tied with a bowline), the end passed through the halter. He is then tied to a corral or snubbing post and left alone to fight the rope to his heart's content, or until such time as he realizes the futility of such action and stands quietly. This process may be repeated two or three days running before actual leading is undertaken.

Working alone, the trainer gives the horse every opportunity to lead willingly; yet if co-operation is not forthcoming, techniques are usually employed that will guarantee results. First, a rope is tied about his middle at the withers, then passed between the front legs to the halter. By pulling on this line the trainer will usually force the colt to walk forward; but should this fail, a figure eight over the rump, across the withers, then under the neck to the halter, is used, and few colts will long resist the pressure of the rope on the rump before stepping forward. These leading lessons are continued until such time as the colt will permit the trainer to lead him about the corral and to stand quietly when tied.

Once broken to lead and having the animal quiet enough to be approached without too much fear of mayhem, he is broken to hobbles, both of the front feet and the tying-up of the left hind foot. This is followed by "sacking" wherein the horse is roughed-up with an empty sack, an old pair of chaps, a saddle blanket, or almost anything that can be slapped around the horse and rubbed on his head and ears. This is continued until he loses all fear of the sack and permits the trainer to pass it between his legs, to rub any portion of his body and to stand quietly to a good dusting.

Saddling is first undertaken in the same small corral and the saddle (with sheepskin lining) is used without saddle blanket. Cabral likes to use the same rigging that will be placed on the finished product whether it be a three-quarter single cinch or a double rig.

"Hell's fire," Cabral snorts. "Lots of breakers use a standard rig, turn the horse over to the owner who puts on a different outfit; the horse sunfishes all over the place, the owner gets bucked off, and the breaker is no good. Nobody's fault really, but the horse wasn't used to the feel of the new rig; he bucks off the owner and the guy that did the breaking is a bum. The only answer is to find out what rig the owner is going to use and start him with that rig and no other."

Once saddled with the cinch drawn snug but not tight enough to cut the horse in two, the process of "neck limbering" is undertaken. Being a four-year-old and having run loose all his life, his neck muscles are set. He has not been driven to lines which would have done much to limber his neck, so the Western breaker resorts to the following: while wearing the saddle he is fitted to a headstall with a large ringed snaffle bit and one rein is snapped into the left ring, the head pulled around and tied to the saddle horn. The horse is then turned loose and left to wander about the corral for an hour. Once he stops fighting the bit and is relaxed, he is considered "ready"; the line is changed to the right side, tied to the horn, and the process is repeated. For those horses who throw themselves and thus roll on the saddle, the saddle is removed, the line tied from bit to tail, and the same "neck limbering" exercise continued. For those animals that develop tender or bleeding mouth corners, rubber or leather guards may be placed over bit rings.

The art of bitting is debatable, depending on what trainer is doing the talking and in what Western locale he is practicing his profession. Some insist on using the hackamore (a bitless headstall that depends on pressure over the nostrils as well as tension on the under side of the jaw) for the first year or two. Others insist that the hackamore be abandoned as quickly as the horse is trustworthy, while still a third school of thought insist that this hackamore business is a waste of time, that the four-year-old should be started with the bit that he is to use throughout his life, whether it be a snaffle, Pelham or spade. All are right, of course, for no one has a corner on the proper market; what works for one man (or horse for that matter) might be worth nothing to another.

The figure eight passed over the rump, across the withers and through the halter ring will make even the most obstinate horse lead.

With a hind foot tied up the colt is "sacked out". Here the youngster is roughed-up with an empty sack until all fear is gone and he will permit the trainer to pass the sack between his legs, to rub any portion of the body.

For the animal that has not been driven to lines, neck limbering is necessary. Here the colt has a line tied from his tail to his headstall which forces him to work in circle, thus limbering the neck muscles.

Yet despite all arguments of the proper method of bitting, they all agree that the colt should first be mounted in a small corral so that the rider has every advantage; the corral should be so small that a bucking horse will have very few good jumps before he hits one fence or the other and gives the rider a chance to resettle his seat in the saddle, his hat on his head.

Wearing the hackamore, or a headstall with the bit of the breaker's choice, the colt is usually saddled with a heavy Western saddle complete with bucking roll. If this is not built into the saddle, a blanket fashioned into a tight roll is tied across the pommel. As has been previously stated, no saddle blanket is used, for blankets have a habit of slipping and usually at exactly the wrong moment. The saddle is placed as far forward on the horse's withers as possible to eliminate the snap-the-whip action that the rider will experience if the saddle is well back on the horse. The cinch is tightened; the horse is walked in circles to shake out the kinks; and then it is tightened again. Now we ask our stomach to please return to its normal resting place from halfway up our esophagus, and prepare to mount.

Most cowboys prefer to work alone in the corral, insisting that even the most experienced assistant causes more injuries than he prevents; that often the horse will concentrate on the assistant rather than upon the rider. Onlookers are discouraged for the same reason; yet this is not always easily accomplished for first mountings can be fun, and family, neighbors, or casual passers-by are often a bit difficult to discourage.

With the animal saddled, with the cinch as tight as we can get it, and with our hat screwed down well on our head, we are as ready as we'll ever be. Should the horse be willing to stand even reasonably still, hobbles are not used. The rider takes the reins well in hand, cheeks the horse (takes a firm hold on the cheek strap of the bridle or hackamore), and pulls the horse's head towards the rider's body. The trainer stands facing the rear, slips his left foot into the stirrup, takes the saddle horn in the right hand, slips into the saddle as quickly and quietly as possible, and slides the right foot into the off stirrup. Now he releases the hand from the cheek strap and takes a firm hold on the lines—one line to each hand.

What happens now? Any one of a hundred things. Perhaps the horse will stand perfectly still, quivering from head to tail. Perhaps he'll try to toss his head to get it down between his front legs, an ideal position from which to launch a buck. Perhaps he'll try to lunge (here the rider might have to exercise considerable pressure on the mouth or hacka-more); to lay down and roll on the rider; to fling himself against the fences. Yet no matter what he does, the rider must have had experience enough to start counter measures to get both himself and the horse out of the mess—and in that order.

Should the horse buck, the experienced rider will spin him. Instead of frantically tugging at both reins (the fault of most beginning break-ers), the rider must pull the horse's head around so that he is made to go in circles. If the rider keeps both his head and his seat, a few turns will do much to bring the horse under control, for bucking and turning seldom go together. Finally, he may be gee-hawed around the corral at what the rider hopes will be a walk or jog, and the first lesson is over. When dismounting, the rider again pulls the horse's head to his left side, cheeks him as he did in mounting and steps off.

In the event that the horse will not stand long enough to permit mounting, a pair of slip hobbles are used. These hobbles tie the horse's front feet together, and once mounted the rider may pull on the rope that, by means of a slip-knot, will release the hobbles. In more desperate cases the left hind foot may be tied up, but most experienced trainers frown on such devices and use them only as a last resort.

Once started the colt is never permitted prolonged rest, certainly never more than a day's rest between mountings. He is usually mounted day after day, the lessons becoming longer and longer. He is not fed a

With a hind foot tied up, first mounting is undertaken. Note that the trainer has a firm hold on the cheek-strap of the headstall, is well forward of kicking hind legs.

Before the hind leg is released the trainer maintains his hold on the cheek strap, thus maintaining control over the animal.

The hind foot is free, and with a line in each hand we are ready for action. Note that the lead-line is tucked loosely into the rider's belt so that if he must step down he may still maintain control of the colt.

heavy grain ration during these initial mountings, and usually four or five "goes" in the small corral are sufficient to warrant working in a larger enclosure or in open country. This decision must be made for each individual horse, some becoming trustworthy enough to go into the open after a week of riding; others require twice that many rides, while still others (not many, thank heavens) seem never to stop their natural tendency to buck and pose a very knotty problem indeed.

For the brave at heart (and no beginner is equipped for such a task) Cabral offers a few safety tips for first ridings. Wear no rings on the fingers, no wrist watches, in fact nothing that can hang you onto the saddle. If you must wear a belt, do not wear one so heavy that it will not break. If your belt is heavy, unbuckle it before mounting so that it cannot drape over the saddle horn and hang you up. Wear heeled boots that will not slip through the stirrups; be sure that they are loose fitting enough so that if you are hung in a stirrup you can slip out of the boot before you are kicked into the next world. If things get tough don't let pride force you to neglect the saddle horn. If you are spinning the horse with one hand, the other should be caressing the horn. A saddle horn in hand is much better than a handful of dirt. Cabral rightly points out that we are interested in breaking the colt to ride, not in giving a contest performance for the benefit of a non-paying audience. Don't use spurs (there are many professional breakers who insist that you should), but if you do, be sure they have short shanks and dull rowels for they could very easily hang you onto the saddle.

Once the colt is trustworthy enough to ride in open country and in the company of other horses, work him on cattle as much as practical. Cattle drives, especially those taking up the better part of a day, are the best possible opportunities for working the prospect. Let him follow along behind the herd for very soon he will learn that his job is to push the tail-enders along, and as he works from side to side, neck rein him and he will unconsciously associate turning with rein pressure on his neck. Cattle will do much to distract his attention from the rider and he will begin to develop the only reason for his existence—cow-sense. Do not ask him to ride the flanks of the herd at the start; let the well-broken cow ponies handle this more delicate job; instead, keep him to the rear where cow-sense and moxie are not required.

As he quiets down, as he starts to concentrate on the cattle, let down about ten feet of your lariat so that he becomes accustomed to the slap of the rope against his neck, and soon you can toss it out before him. He should stand for this sort of nonsense on a reasonably loose rein, and it should not require too many cattle drives until he is neck reining well and has little fear of the rope. As he progresses he should be taught to back, to stand with reins down and without being tied or held; and if he is to be used as a rope horse, he should be taught to slide to a halt as the rope is thrown.

When starting the prospective roping horse, the rider should select a "doggie" calf—a slow, small, young animal. The lariat is fitted with a "breakaway" device that will loosen from the calf's neck immediately after being caught, and, of course, the rope should not be tied hard and fast to the saddle horn; instead it should be dallied so that the rider has a chance to let go should the "breakaway" fail.

Before actual roping without a "breakaway" is attempted, the horse should be worked in a small confined area, the rider throwing his loop at an imaginary calf, pulling the horse to a stop, jumping off and racing down the line, all the while tugging on the rope and commanding the horse to back up, keeping all slack from the line. A neck rope is used on the horse (the lariat passed through so that when the rider pulls on the rope it pulls the horse's head towards him) thus forcing the horse to face the "calf" at all times.

As we undertake actual roping we again select a "doggie" calf, one that we are sure we can catch and one that will not put up too much of a fight for your young horse. This work is best accomplished in a medium-size arena, one fenced tightly so that our calf cannot escape should we miss our loop, or should our horse act up and make accurate throwing difficult.

Once the calf is caught and our colt is brought to a sudden stop, we jump off and pull ourselves hand over hand to the bawling calf, all the while insisting that the horse keep backing up to keep all slack from the line. We will have to rope many calves (or the same calf many times) before any manner of perfection can be expected, and a bit of patience at this stage of training will be most rewarding in the days to come.

The cutting horse, now the rage of many Western shows and rodeos, has been developed to a magnificent point of perfection and many are rightfully valued in the $5000 and up class. They are usually Quarter Horses and are the cream of all Western performers. Together with excellent mouths, handiness, and the ability to turn within their own length, all top cutting horses are blessed with a great deal of cow-sense.

Horses will vary greatly in this quality, and the beginner must be warned that every cow horse does not have the makings of a cutting horse any more than every Thorobred three-year-old is horse enough to be entered in the Derby. With some Western shows offering a dozen classes for cutting horses, it is natural for many beginners to want to enter these events. Yet it must be remembered that the cutting horse must rein with the best of them and above all he must enjoy his work; he should lay back his ears and take on the cow as a competitive adversary, and if he does not display this real interest, he'll never make a top cutting horse regardless of reining ability, conformation, breeding, or the desire of his owner.

Before actual roping is attempted, the horse is taught to stand back from the imaginary calf by the trainer who pulls on the rope giving the command, "Stand!".

Whip breaking is quite common in Western training. Note that the animal has approached his trainer and stands still awaiting instructions.

Whip breaking is a common practice in the Western method of training, and a very good thing it is. Two methods are practiced and two separate aims are strived for. Parade horses, pleasure horses and trail horses are, through whip breaking, taught to come on command, to walk immediately up to the trainer, and to stand with his head instead of his heels towards his master. Working stock horses are taught to face the trainer but not to walk towards him. Calf roping specialists must never approach the horseman and all manner of working stock horses are discouraged from following the master about the corral.

To whip-break the non-working animal, the colt is fitted to a stout halter and taken to the small breaking corral. The only equipment necessary is a light buggy whip and a halter shank. With the trainer facing the animal, he gives the command, "come!" at the same time putting light pressure on the halter rope. If the horse does not step up to the trainer at once, he is flicked lightly across the cannon bones with the whip, and the command is repeated. Most horses learn this lesson very quickly for the trainer has every advantage—the halter shank, the small corral, the whip. After a few lessons the halter shank is removed and the horse worked loose and cracked with the whip until he learns to come without hesitancy. A well whip-broken horse will always thereafter face his master when the master enters the corral and will stand while either halter or bridle is put into place. How much better than that brute who habitually rushes to the nearest corner, buries his head between his front legs and dares the trainer to come in and get him.

Working stock horses are usually whip-broken in the same small corral but without the halter. The whip is flicked at their cannon bones until they learn to face the trainer, but never to walk up to him. This is not a difficult thing to teach the horse, and a little patience will do much to whip-break him to the desired point—to turn towards the trainer and to stand still.

From now on progress in training depends entirely upon horse and trainer. The parade horse may be taught head and tail carriage and to "walk out" with good stride. The roping horse will be continued in his training and taught to break from the barrier should he be destined for the contest arena, and the cutting horse will be worked on faster and larger cattle until he reaches the peak of his potentiality. The pleasure horse will be schooled in whatever gaits his owner desires to give his trainer a first-class ride; in other words, to become the "pleasure" that his name implies.

CHAPTER V

FEEDING THE HORSE

"THAT man eats like a horse." How often have we heard this statement to indicate gluttony in the human, and as with many a sage utterance, this too is highly erroneous. Better had it been, "That horse eats like a man," for pound for pound man's uncontrollable appetite makes the horse seem a rank amateur in the gourmand's world.

Most horsemen, even those of considerable experience, are continually amazed when they learn that the average human eats sixteen times his weight per year; that the supposed glutton, the horse, eats but half that amount—eight times his weight.

"Oh," says the prospective mother as she reaches for a second or third helping from the festive board, "I'm eating for two." Conclusive evidence of well-regulated experiments on horse feeding prove that the mare does not require any excessive feeding during the last eighty-five days of her pregnancy, that this additional feed is unnecessary due to the slowing down of her normal activities. Consequently, the mare that is properly fed seldom has trouble producing a foal; and there are more Caesarean operations in Hollywood in a single day than in the horse world in many a year. Strangely enough, mortality rates of both mare and foal on well-regulated farms compare very favorably with that of the human in the United States and are far superior to those of many a foreign land.

This is in no way meant to imply that the horse can be self-fed, that he can be turned loose in a granary and be permitted to eat his fill (as in the case of the hog), for unlike the hog he will kill himself even quicker than the heavy eating human. He hasn't the intelligence to know when to stop, and his feeding must be regulated by the trainer who should expend considerable intelligence and caution in controlling the horse's appetite.

Observation of each horse as an individual is far more important than the weighing of feed, for horses differ so much in temperament, working habits, and in body weight that anything specific that we may say must be used as a guide rather than as an indisputable recommendation. Yet enough experimentation has been conducted by our leading agricultural colleges to produce a comprehensible guide which will give the horse feeder a starting point from which he may deviate, depending on the horse in question.

Feeds are classified into roughages and concentrates. Roughages will include hay, pasturage, etc., and are normally high in fiber and low in digestible nutrients. Concentrates, oats, barley, corn, etc., are the reverse, high in digestible nutrients with a low fiber content. It should go without saying that the horse requires almost unlimited roughage to produce bulk for the stomach and that concentrates are fed to produce growth, to keep up body weight and, of course, should be increased for those animals that are doing hard work, are in intense training, or are being fitted for the show ring.

Along this line let us examine some recommended rations suggested by Professor Carrol Howell of the University of California and one time manager of the Kellog Arabian Stud Farm. These rations are computed for a thousand pound horse at medium work. Medium work for the saddle horse might well be defined as at least ten hours of riding per week spread out over three exercise periods, and the ration should be increased or decreased in direct proportion to the weight of the animal.

Ration 1			*Ration 3*	
Oat hay	12 pounds		Grass hay	10 pounds
Alfalfa hay	3 pounds		Alfalfa hay	3 pounds
Rolled barley	5 pounds		Oats	5 pounds
Wheat bran	1 pound		Rolled barley	3 pounds

Ration 2			*Ration 4*	
Oat hay	10 pounds		Oat hay	8 pounds
Alfalfa hay	4 pounds		Grass hay	6 pounds
Rolled barley	4 pounds		Rolled barley	4 pounds
Oats	3 pounds		Oats	2 pounds
			Wheat bran	1 pound

In localities where timothy-and-clover hay is available at reasonable prices, it may be substituted for oat hay and in very cold climates a small amount of cracked corn (considered a "hot" feed whereas oats is considered a "cool" feed) may be used in place of some of the rolled barley or oat allowance. On days of idleness, or should the animal show the effects of overfeeding, the concentrates may be cut in half and the hay allowance increased. All grain placed before the horse should be consumed within a half-hour after feeding, and if the animal's appetite is not keen enough for this rapid clean-up, the concentrates should be cut down until his appetite again demands more grain.

Overfeeding has ruined more horses than all equine diseases combined. "Hell's fire," snorted a leading veterinary of our acquaintance who practices in a location wherein both horses and owners are listed in one blue book or another, "I'm sending two sons through college on fees collected for prescribing harmless powder and a reducing diet. Sure it's a racket, but no more so than a lot of M.D.'s who are making fortunes from reducing gimmicks. This horse business is getting to the pet class. Every call that I receive (especially those in the middle of the night) is an 'emergency' and more than half of them are digestive disturbances caused by overfeeding. The only saving grace is that the horse is a tough customer and is darned hard to kill even though many of his owners are making a determined effort to dispatch him to the green pastures."

For the animal that is being fed an adequate diet and is still not doing well the owner should consult a veterinarian with the possibility of internal parasites in mind. Personally, we worm young, growing horses four times per year. At eight years twice per year seems sufficient, and for the aged horse—upwards from ten years old—we find that once per year is ample. Horses, it appears to the experienced, will always have a parasite problem, the severity of the manifestation depending on local conditions, climate, and feed used. Old horses seem to learn to live with them and therefore require less worming than does the younger animal. Then, too, new parasites keep popping up, and many have built up a resistance to medication in much the same manner as the common housefly has overcome his onetime mortal enemy, D.D.T.

The quality of feeds is far more important than the amount fed. If, for example, all oat hay contained the exact same chemical analysis, hard and fast recommendations could be given for animal feeding. Unfortunately, this is far from the case. Good quality hay and cereal grains produced on healthy soils will surpass the average standards and will do much for horse nutrition. Conversely, poor quality hay and grains produced on worn-out land loaded with parasites will starve a horse regardless of how heavily the animal is fed. The animal's stomach just is not large enough to take in the amount of poor feed needed to produce the required digestible protein and the total digestible nutrients necessary to sustain life.

Many commercial feeds are on the market that answer this quality problem, and if cost is of little consideration they may be used very successfully. They are sold under a number of trade names by our leading feed companies, ready-mixed, requiring nothing but placing them in the feed box. Some are highly palatable and horses do very well on them, but costs are high and are practically prohibitive for those feeding any number of horses on a restricted budget. Here the owner is paying not only for the actual feed in the sack, but for the sack itself as well as advertising costs, the cost of mixing and in some cases a fantastic profit for the feed company. This is not necessarily true of all commercial feeds for some are priced within reason, are high in quality, and are the answer to feeding problems for those who are feeding one or two horses and are not sufficiently experienced to purchase concentrates of good quality for home mixing.

The same caution must be used in the purchase of mineral mixtures. The horse requires salt and must have it available at all times. Some feeders prefer to include two pounds of ground salt for every one hundred pounds of grain mixture while others prefer to place a salt block in the feed box or in the pasture. Either is good practice.

Yet the feeder must be warned that many commercial mineral mixtures are offered that are long on salesmanship, high in price, and of little value. There is usually nothing in these mixtures that will actually injure the animal; yet the good that they will do is questionable and seldom is in line with the salesman's claims. Some fantastic claims are made in their behalf and the feeder will do well to scrutinize the actual worth of these products in relationship to the price asked.

Reduced to its simplest equation, the feeding of the horse develops into an exercise in common sense, keen observation and the ability to say "No" to that animal that begs, whinnies, and pleads for just one more helping from the oat bin. Of these, the observant eye is perhaps the paramount factor.

Not long ago a State Experiment Station was hastily called by a harried horseman who complained that even though his horses were grazing on a mountain meadow which he considered ample pasturage, they were losing weight rapidly and that he feared for the worst. He had ample cause for worry, for by the time the experts arrived, some of the younger animals were weaving as they grazed, and upon the recommendations of the people from the Station they were at once removed to lower pasture and fed a grain ration to rebuild their strength.

Next, a quantity of the feed of the meadow was clipped and gathered, taken to the Experiment Station, and under scientific conditions fed to a number of animals. Chemical analysis of both feed and feces were taken and carefully evaluated. Results were startling, for the analysis showed a decided minus factor—the feed did not produce enough nourishment to produce the necessary energy for the animal to clip, chew and digest the pasturage, let alone to produce maintenance for the horse.

"These animals would have done better on a concrete tennis court," was the conclusion of the report. "If they had been confined to a small enclosure, at least they would have saved the energy that they expended in their frantic efforts to take in enough feed to sustain life."

Yes, common sense, coupled with an observing eye is the answer to the feeding of the horse—as it is to human feeding. Fortunately, it is far easier to apply these facilities to our mounts than to ourselves.

CHAPTER VI

TO HORSE

AND NOW, to horse, and all the contradictions of the previous chapters. We have emphasized soundness in the horse. Of course, a sound horse is more desirable than one of even a slight blemish. As with the dollar, the sounder the better, but it's a dollar nevertheless; and as one expert (of the horse not the dollar) points out: "Give me a mature horse with a splint or two. He didn't get them standing around in hock deep straw in a fancy box stall. He got them doing a good job of work for somebody, and he must be willing to put out or he wouldn't have come up with a splint."

Along similar lines, the horse of high spirit who insists on wanting to do more than is being asked and kicks up his heels in protest when he is admonished, is a far more satisfactory ride than the "soldier" horse who does a little less than asked of him. This is especially true should you be horseman enough to keep the spirited animal under at least a semblance of control.

All phases of horsemanship from breeding, training and finally riding, reduced to their common denominator, depend on point of view. Some years ago we managed to raise an excellent Thorobred

143

filly on the bottle (a most complicated formula) when her imported dam died during parturition. We were justly proud of this accomplishment having failed in the same endeavor several times previously and, with a bit of smugness, we told Professor Howell of this phenomena as we walked about the University Farm, at Davis, California.

"Oh, you didn't do so very much," said Howell, deflating our ego. "After all, there isn't much of a problem in bottle-feeding a foal."

"The hell there isn't," was our reply. "We've tried it several times and we don't know too many people that have managed it with a Thorobred."

"All you actually need is a fresh goat," the Professor came back. "You put the goat in a stall with the orphan and they'll be excellent company for each other. When it's time to feed the foal you take a little milk from the goat, give it to the foal through a nipple, rinse both nipple and bottle and let it go at that. No complicated formulas to mix, no refrigeration problem, no bottles to sterilize and warm up before each feeding. It works. Simple, isn't it?"

"Well, yes," was our weak reply. "I suppose that it does. But you've always taught us that a milk-producing animal must be completely milked out at each milking. Wouldn't these partial milkings be injurious to the milk goat?"

"Young man," Howell was smiling. "Concentrate for a moment. What was our problem. Was it, 'How to raise an orphan foal,' or was it, 'How to milk a goat'?"

Yes, all manner of horsemanship depends entirely on point of view, and it must be your point of view and no other. It matters little what your friends think or say about your mount. It matters even less if he is a spotted mule, if he suits you and you suit him. Except for the professional who makes his living with horses, horsemanship in all its ramifications is a sport; and if we cannot enjoy our mount, if we are continually fighting the brute, there's nothing for it but to either change horses or take up croquet.

As in all endeavors, be it sport, work or just plain and fancy living, the entire problem is a highly personal one and one that must be worked out by each individual. Shortly before the United States entry into World War II we reported to Colonel Hans Klophfer, an old line cavalry officer, ex-master of Hounds and a first rate horseman, officer and gentleman. That he was feared by all junior officers (and we were very junior) was such a well-known fact that we shook a bit as we watched him inspecting our 201 file.

"Reserve officer!" he growled.

He jerked off his heavy tortoise-shell glasses and gave us a stern glare. He took inventory from the top of our head to the soles of our shoes and never had a young stud in the show ring had a more thorough going-over. He slapped his glasses back onto his face, picked up our file and again gave it a perfunctory reading.

"Summer camps; staff work by correspondence; no service with troops." He was barking now. "So far you've been pushing thousands and thousands of troops all over the map, but only on paper. Now, I tell you what I'm going to do with you. I'm going to give you a platoon, a very small platoon, and you are going to learn to push them around by hand . . . That's all! Excused!"

Although Colonel Klophfer's advice was being given to a young civilian-soldier, it is about the best possible advice that could be given the young horseman. One may read all the books on horses ever published, including our minor offerings, but in the last analysis you must "learn to push them around by hand." You must learn by experience; by the careful study of instruction; by learning to imitate your betters. You must learn by picking yourself up out of the dirt; by remounting and starting again. There is no other way.

APPENDICES AND INDEX

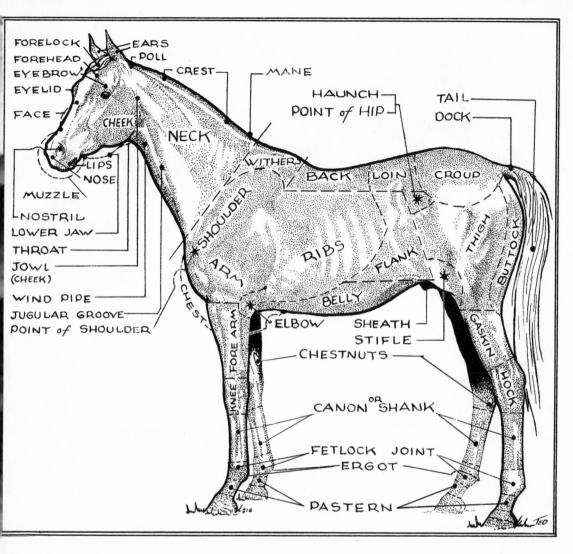

Anatomy and Nomenclature

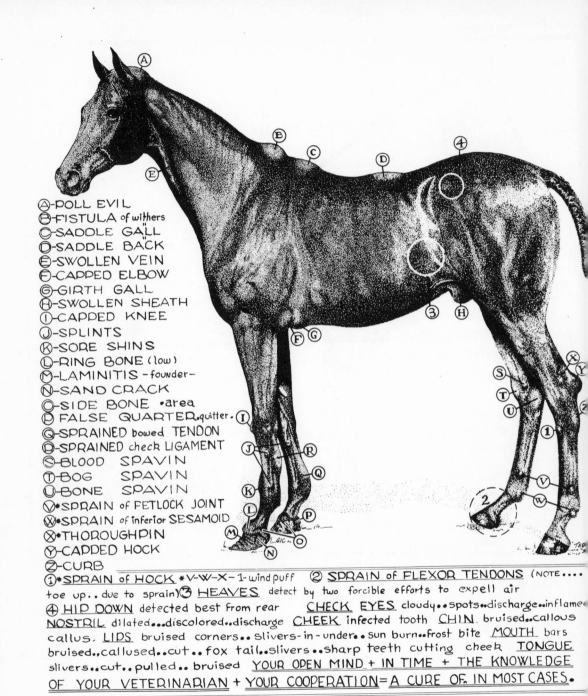

Ⓐ-POLL EVIL
Ⓑ-FISTULA of withers
Ⓒ-SADDLE GALL
Ⓓ-SADDLE BACK
Ⓔ-SWOLLEN VEIN
Ⓕ-CAPPED ELBOW
Ⓖ-GIRTH GALL
Ⓗ-SWOLLEN SHEATH
Ⓘ-CAPPED KNEE
Ⓙ-SPLINTS
Ⓚ-SORE SHINS
Ⓛ-RING BONE (low)
Ⓜ-LAMINITIS -founder-
Ⓝ-SAND CRACK
Ⓞ-SIDE BONE •area
Ⓟ-FALSE QUARTER•quitter•
Ⓠ-SPRAINED bowed TENDON
Ⓡ-SPRAINED check LIGAMENT
Ⓢ-BLOOD SPAVIN
Ⓣ-BOG SPAVIN
Ⓤ-BONE SPAVIN
Ⓥ*SPRAIN of FETLOCK JOINT
Ⓦ*SPRAIN of inferior SESAMOID
Ⓧ*THOROUGHPIN
Ⓨ-CAPPED HOCK
Ⓩ-CURB
①*SPRAIN of HOCK *V-W-X-1-windpuff ②SPRAIN of FLEXOR TENDONS (NOTE....
toe up..due to sprain)③HEAVES detect by two forcible efforts to expell air
④HIP DOWN detected best from rear   CHECK EYES cloudy..spots..discharge..inflame
NOSTRIL dilated...discolored..discharge CHEEK infected tooth CHIN bruised..callous
callus. LIPS bruised corners.. slivers-in-under.. sun burn..frost bite MOUTH bars
bruised..callused..cut..fox tail..slivers..sharp teeth cutting cheek TONGUE
slivers..cut..pulled.. bruised YOUR OPEN MIND + IN TIME + THE KNOWLEDGE
OF YOUR VETERINARIAN + YOUR COOPERATION = A CURE OF IN MOST CASES.

Visual Symptoms

FIRST AID FOR HORSES

FIRST AID for horses should be exactly the same as first aid for humans. First aid in the animal kingdom should not presume to replace the services of a competent veterinarian any more than first aid for the human is intended to replace the specialized services of the medical doctor. Quackery in the animal kingdom is fully as dangerous as is quackery when practiced by various "healers," and most states consider this animal quackery fully as illegal as they do the practicing of medicine without a license. Yet, first aid for horses has saved the life of many a fine animal and has certainly done much to preserve soundness. We therefore choose to stick with first aid rather than in listing a lot of common ailments and their supposed cures.

BROKEN BONES: Keep the animal as quiet and comfortable as possible. If the break is such that a splint can be applied, do so until the veterinarian can be summoned.

BRUISES: Hot Epsom salts packs may be used as may many of the commercial abrasives. Massage may be useful after the bruise has healed.

COLIC: Colic, or the common bellyache, is common with horses. There is much discomfort, biting at the flank is often indicative of colic, and as the horse cannot vomit, this may well be a serious condition. Keep the animal on his feet. Do not permit him to lie down or to thrash about. Always keep a bottle of colic remedy (prepared by a veterinarian) on hand for such emergencies. Do not give baking soda, for this may produce gas that could prove dangerous.

CRACKED HOOF: A cracked hoof will take up to eight months to grow out. A good blacksmith may be a help and a hoof oil may be applied to soften the foot. Mud baths are often recommended.

151

DISTEMPER IN COLTS: This is an infectious disease found in young horses. Keep the youngster warm, out of drafts, and cover him with a blanket in cold climates. Speed in obtaining help here is of paramount importance.

FOUNDER: Founder causes an intense congestion in the feet and is usually caused by overfeeding, permitting undigested feed to pass from the stomach into the bowels. Do not permit the animal access to water and stand him in mud if possible. Call the veterinarian at once.

HEMORRHAGE: Hemorrhage due to wire cuts, injury or accident is common enough with horses. Keep the wound clean, do not permit the horse to roll on bedding, and in severe cases apply a pressure bandage. Do not, under any conditions, apply a tourniquet.

IMPACTION: Impaction in the horse causes more deaths than any other condition. Poor teeth are often the cause, with large masses of half-digested material accumulating in the bowel causing a partial paralysis. Do not give colic remedies, give plenty of water, keep comfortable and send for the expert.

NAIL IN FOOT: Be sure to mark the spot when the nail is removed so that treatment may be undertaken. Use tincture of iodine, and be sure to pour it into the wound as soon as the nail is removed.

SADDLE GALLS: These stubborn sores are the result of overheating under saddle blankets. If a core has developed in the galled spot this may be removed by an expert and usually the trouble will clear up. However, watch all saddle blankets; do not permit them to become matted.

SLEEPING SICKNESS: Encephalomyelitis is a common horse disease, although there is a vaccine that is nearly 100 per cent effective and all horse owners should have their animals inoculated annually. In the event that the disease does strike it will be noted that the victim becomes dull, loses appetite and acts sleepy. Cold packs may be applied to the head, and a veterinarian should be sent for at once. Full recovery is rare, yet some total cures have been accomplished if the victim receives aid in time.

PULLED TENDON: This is a very serious condition and is certainly no place for the amateur practitioner. Apply cold compresses with belladonna lotion. Consult your veterinarian at once. He may recommend "firing" but this must be done by an expert's expert. Every veterinarian does not qualify in this regard.

MONDAY MORNING SICKNESS: Azuturia, commonly known as Monday Morning Sickness, is the result of heavy feeding of the horse that has been idle and then put to hard work. The animal will go down behind and will stiffen at the joints. Do not move the horse unless necessary but if he must be moved do so very slowly and send for an expert.

It is admitted that we have not been of too much help in this section for it is our belief that more harm than good is done by well-meaning horse owners and "friends." Great advances have been made in the veterinary profession, and the horse owner should take full advantage of these advancements.

As one topflight veterinarian pointed out recently at a meeting of a horse club, there are three types of horsemen:

(1) The owner who has a pet, knows little, but admits it.

(2) The know-it-all. He has been around horses just long enough to have become a complete authority. He knows all the cures for all ailments and is a dangerous human to have around.

(3) The true horseman who knows his horses from pole to tail. He knows enough to call the veterinarian at once, knowing that speed is of the essence; that there is little to be gained by trying all home remedies first and then sending for the expert to officiate at the funeral.

It seems logical enough to assume that if our horse is worth feeding he is worth the best of care. Do what you can for the animal's comfort until help can arrive. Then listen to your veterinarian. Do as he says. When he says rest a horse for six months, rest him for six months even though you might think a lesser rest period would be sufficient. Above all don't listen to your "friends." They mean well, of course, but you would not take their advice about the care of your child. Why do it with your horse?

DETECTING THE AGE

OF A HORSE

When a foal is born the premolars (baby teeth, milk teeth) can be felt under the membrane. The first pair of teeth to appear in both upper and lower jaws are the center Nipper (Fig. 1, N or No. 1 tooth). They appear from one week to fourteen days after birth. The second pair of Nippers or Middle teeth (Fig. 1, M or No. 2 tooth) appear between five weeks and three months. The third and last pair of premolars are the outside Corner teeth (Fig. 1, C or No. 3 tooth) and appear at six to nine months. Now that the foal has a complete set of premolars, we detect age by the wear.

A new tooth has a protective covering over all. The dish or cup (soft center of the tooth) is heavily capped (Fig. 2 A). This protective covering is stained a dark color by the food juices (Fig. 2 B). The outside ridge, being higher, narrower and more thinly coated, loses its stain much sooner, leaving the dark spot or cup (Fig. 2 B); and as the tooth wears, the spot or cup becomes smaller until all the stained protective coating is worn smooth exposing the hard white rings of the tooth (Fig. 2 D).

At nine months, with a complete set of premolars, the spot on N or No. 1 tooth should be quite small. The M or No. 2 has a larger spot and the new corner C or No. 3 is just beginning to show signs of wear.

Between one, and one and half years the spot leaves N or No. 1. Between one and a half and two years the spot leaves M or No. 2, and soon thereafter the spot leaves C or No. 3. The premolars (milk teeth) are now wearing down and are being pushed out by the new permanent teeth which are growing down to replace the premolars.

At two and a half years a foal starts shedding its milk teeth, so at this time the N or No. 1 teeth shed and are replaced by the new permanent teeth which grow to full size at about three years.

154

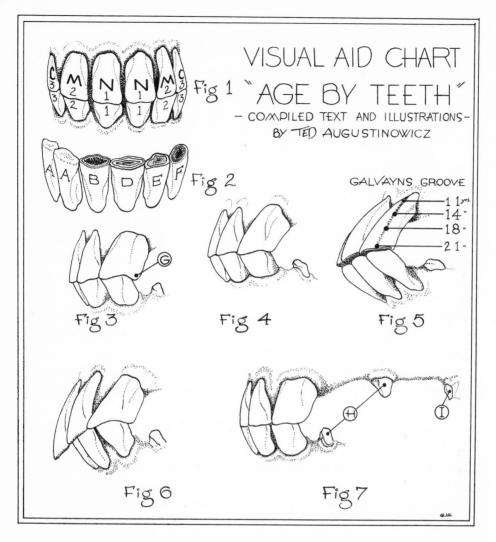

VISUAL AID CHART
Fig 1 "AGE BY TEETH"
– COMPILED TEXT AND ILLUSTRATIONS –
BY TED AUGUSTINOWICZ

Fig 2

GALVAYNS GROOVE
— 11 yrs.
— 14 "
— 18 "
— 21 "

Fig 3

Fig 4

Fig 5

Fig 6

Fig 7

At three and a half years the M or No. 2 teeth shed and are replaced by permanent teeth which become full size at four years.

And last, in a four-and-a-half-year old, the corner tooth C or No. 3 drops out and is replaced by the permanent tooth growing out to full size in a five-year-old (Fig. 7). At this time a horse is called a "full-mouthed horse," a five-year-old (Fig. 7). From this time we consider the progressing age again by the wearing of the teeth, looking for the appearance of the white rings and the diminishing dark spots (cups).

To detect the six-year-old mouth, look for the following: the Corner No. 3, being the newest tooth, has the largest black spot; the Middle or No. 2 a smaller spot; and the No. 1 Nipper, being the first to start wearing, has the smallest black spot or (cup).

At seven years the No. 1 tooth or N loses its black spot (cup), exposing the hard white rings (Fig. 2 D).

At eight years the No. 2 or M black spot (cup) is worn, exposing the hard white rings (Fig. 2 D).

At nine the Corner or No. 3 tooth loses the black spot (cup) (Fig. 2 D). At this time a horse is called "a smooth-mouthed horse"—the cups are gone.

(Note the wide oval form of tooth (Fig. 2 D) indicating a young mouth). From nine to ten years the appearance of the oval changes and becomes narrower with age and wear giving the white rings a squeezed triangular appearance (Fig. 2 E). Generally, after ten years (Fig. 4) the teeth take on a slanting appearance from age. Also, at ten years, a groove appears in the Corner tooth No. 3 called the Galvayns Groove. This groove extends downward with the growth of the tooth and is the surest way of detecting approximate advanced age (Fig. 5). With advancing age, the teeth change from the squeezed triangular shape (Fig. 2 E) to the round shape with a dark holed center (Fig. 2 F) increasing the slanting effect (Fig. 5).

Many seven-year-olds have (Fig. 3 G) the "seven-year-old notch," which is worn smooth at eight (Fig. 4). Compare Fig. 3 G and Fig. 4. In some cases the notch remains until nine years. Generally, slanted teeth cause the notch. Compare Fig. 7 as the mouth of a five-year-old with Fig. 3 "the seven year notch," notch due to growth of tooth and uneven wear caused by slight slant.

The Canine (Tushe, Fig. 7 H) appear at four and a half years and are full sized at five years. The Canine is seldom, if ever, in a mare's mouth.

The Wolf Tooth (Fig. 7 I) is a premolar or No. 1 tooth and appears between five and six months. This has but one root and sometimes remains permanently or sheds at two and one half years, not to be replaced.

The age of a malformed mouth such as the Parrot Shaped Mouth (Fig. 6) is detected by a lot of practical common sense (which applies to detecting age in any horse) due to so many conditions to which a horse is exposed. Generally, however, the system described here is favored.

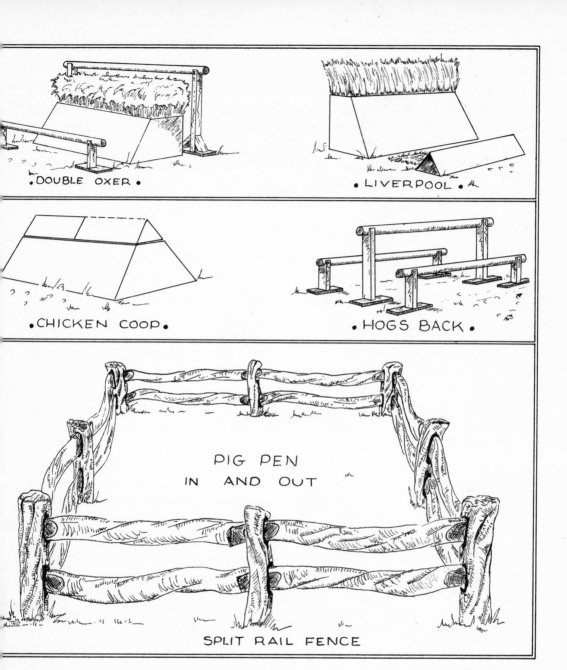

. DOUBLE OXER .

. LIVERPOOL .

. CHICKEN COOP .

. HOGS BACK .

PIG PEN
IN AND OUT

SPLIT RAIL FENCE

Jump Types

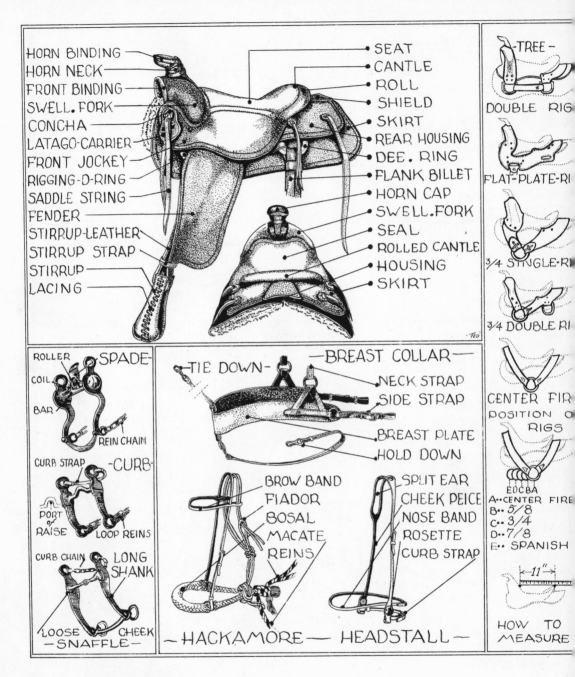

HORN BINDING
HORN NECK
FRONT BINDING
SWELL. FORK
CONCHA
LATAGO-CARRIER
FRONT JOCKEY
RIGGING-D-RING
SADDLE STRING
FENDER
STIRRUP-LEATHER
STIRRUP STRAP
STIRRUP
LACING

SEAT
CANTLE
ROLL
SHIELD
SKIRT
REAR HOUSING
DEE. RING
FLANK BILLET
HORN CAP
SWELL.FORK
SEAL
ROLLED CANTLE
HOUSING
SKIRT

-TREE-
DOUBLE RIG
FLAT-PLATE-RI
3/4 SINGLE-RI
3/4 DOUBLE RI

CENTER FIR
POSITION O
RIGS

EDCBA
A··CENTER FIRE
B·· 5/8
C·· 3/4
D·· 7/8
E·· SPANISH

11"

HOW TO
MEASURE

ROLLER   SPADE-
COIL
BAR
REIN CHAIN

CURB STRAP   -CURB-
PORT
o
RAISE   LOOP REINS

CURB CHAIN   LONG
SHANK

LOOSE   CHEEK
-SNAFFLE-

-TIE DOWN-   -BREAST COLLAR-
NECK STRAP
SIDE STRAP

BREAST PLATE
HOLD DOWN

BROW BAND
FIADOR
BOSAL
MACATE
REINS

SPLIT EAR
CHEEK PEICE
NOSE BAND
ROSETTE
CURB STRAP

-HACKAMORE-   -HEADSTALL-

Western Tack

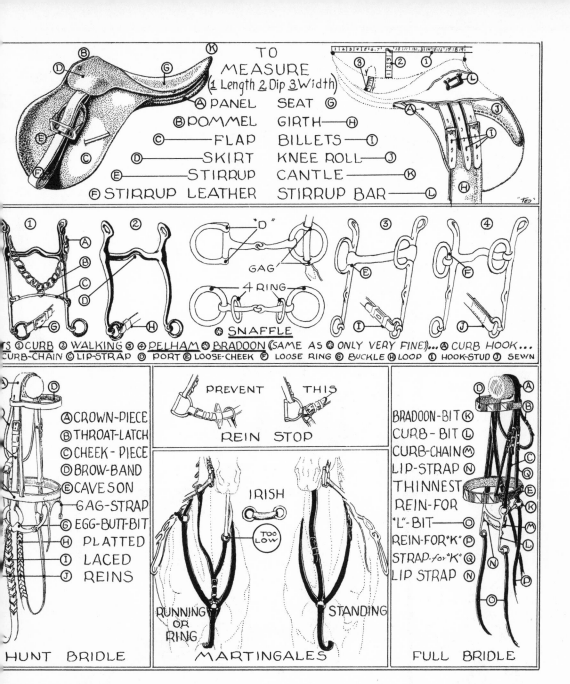

Eastern Tack

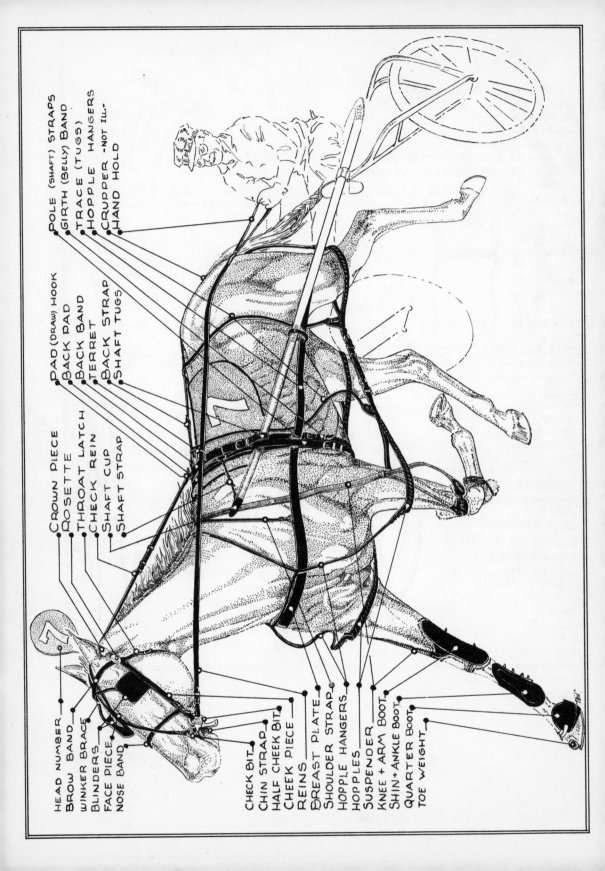

POLE (SHAFT) STRAPS
GIRTH (BELLY) BAND
TRACE (TUGS)
HOPPLE HANGERS
CRUPPER -NOT ILL-
HAND HOLD

PAD (DRAW) HOOK
BACK PAD
BACK BAND
TERRET
BACK STRAP
SHAFT TUGS

CROWN PIECE
ROSETTE
THROAT LATCH
CHECK REIN
SHAFT CUP
SHAFT STRAP

HEAD NUMBER
BROW BAND
WINKER BRACE
BLINDERS
FACE PIECE
NOSE BAND

CHECK BIT
CHIN STRAP
HALF CHECK BIT
CHEEK PIECE
REINS
BREAST PLATE
SHOULDER STRAP
HOPPLE HANGERS
HOPPLES
SUSPENDER
KNEE + ARM BOOT
SHIN + ANKLE BOOT
QUARTER BOOT
TOE WEIGHT

INDEX

161